To this

V

iScream:

From Strangers with Love

Jo Burke

First published by EZE Publications as an eBook in July 2015.

First published in paperback by EZE Publications on Lulu in July 2015.

Based on true events but the names of the characters in this publication have been changed in order to protect their identity. Any resemblance to any other real persons, living or dead, is purely coincidental.

978-0-9932415-3-6

Printed by Biddles Books, King's Lynn, Norfolk PE32 1SF

Jo Burke is a born and bred South East Londoner who still insists on living there. She's an actress, comedienne and writer. A "So You Think That's Funny?" finalist and a regular on the stand up circuit, this book was published to coincide with her fifth show 'iScream' which features some excerpts from the content herein.

"Tomorrow is just a word not a guarantee"

Jo Burke

REVIEWS FOR iSCREAM THE STAGE SHOW

* * * * Everything Theatre

"Jo is brilliantly funny, and this heartwarming show will leave you with a smile on your face many hours after you leave the theatre."

Highly Recommended Show - Fringe Review

"Burke is a talented, creative performer, confident and engaging. She is charming and the audience cannot help but love her. She involves them every step of the way and they love standing up and singing the finale with her".

Miranda Hart has strong competition - Remote Goat

"Jo Burke is certainly a talented performer with some wonderful impressions up her sleeve. Honest, unapologetic and charming. I'm looking forward to more work from this great comedienne."

DEDICATION

For Mum and Dad who met and fell in love at The Yorkshire Grey Ballroom, Eltham.

Sadly now a McDonald's where you'd struggle to find real food let alone real love ...

Love conquers all except poverty and toothache.

Mae West

iScream

A Brief History of Jo

I am born! Get me, all Charles Dickens! Don't panic this is by no means a Dickensian novel. If it were, my name would be Ms Cynthia Cyn Ickle or Ms Loveless or Ms Getnone. Anyway, don't interrupt. Now, where was I? Oh yes, I am born - okay, so I come into this world upside down and backwards. Start as you mean to go on! I have the umbilical cord wrapped around my neck, so had I swum in the direction of mum's special water feature in the normal fashion I would have died. As an unborn baby, milling about in the foetal sack - as one does - I heard horrible predictions about the "outside". Things like "house prices will soar out of control" or "two in three marriages end in divorce" or "Bush re-elected as President". On hearing these or similar whisperings I determined that being born would be risky. Being born would mean I'd have to (a) wait to die of old age or (b) take up a ludicrously dangerous sport and hope that I escape the mortal world quickly! Or worse (c) lead a humdrum existence and suffer depression, eventually commit suicide, which I realistically wouldn't be able to do until a certain age and by that point it would be even more upsetting for my parents and family. I thought the only way to bail out was to strangle myself using the only thing available under the circumstances. Damn those interfering do-gooder doctors. If they hadn't stuck their scalpels in, it could have saved me all manner of embarrassments and suffering. Saying that, actually I expect my mother was rather relieved I was an emergency caesarean - I weighed in at a mighty 9lb 7oz.

Without doubt that's gonna chaff. Michelin owe me a stack of royalties. Boy was I a chubber.

Anyway enough of suicidal foetuses and on with the book - which contains a few chapters that by their nature are slightly diarised. I should therefore explain I'm certainly no Bridget Jones. There are some similarities I will admit. I'm thirty-three and do not currently have a boyfriend. I've never been married. I don't have children. There the similarities end. I'm currently living with my mum (who couldn't prepare a turkey curry buffet if her life depended on it) and one of my brothers (who has just been through a tough split with his long term partner) in the suburbs. Unlike Bridge, I cannot afford to live on my own in a rather lovely pad slap bang in the middle of central London. I actually always wondered just how our long suffering heroine made ends meet. I suspect mummy and daddy paid for it.

I do not, sadly, have Huge Grunt and the simpering D'ars-licky vying for my attention. Cue needle being scraped over record. I would at this point consider myself lucky to have one peg-toothed old tramp fighting with himself over me.

Let me bring you quickly up to speed: At the age of sixteen I left school (a rough South London comprehensive) having only ever been beaten up once (quite an achievement). It was a rough school then, so goodness only knows what it's like now and frankly I dread to think. Former famous pupils include Boy George and a teenage murderer (who was in my very same year). To give you an idea of the prospects the school thought we had ahead of us, let me tell you who they brought in to give us a talk about their "profession" in our final year. Was it a journalist you ask? Perhaps it was a nurse? Then it was a policeman, social worker or a bank manager or or ... Let me stop you there. It was none of the aforementioned. The "careers" presentation in our school was by a ...

TESCO'S CHECK OUT GIRL!

I swear it's true. Bravo Thatch! Way to go girl! Well, it simply wouldn't do for any of us "working class" children to go to university. Perhaps get above our station and maybe want to change our lot in life. We might start to think the unthinkable and decide not to work for anyone at all and set up our own companies or even worse have our own ... dare I say it? HAVE OUR OWN IDEAS! No. Far better that none of us are even told about further education. Pack us all off to the supermarkets and with any luck we'll be up the duff before we can announce "price check on isle furteen please". Keep us too poor and uneducated to either notice or do anything about the government's evil plans for the country. HA HA HA HA! Cue sinister laugh. AHHH AHH AHHA. Cut sinister laugh. Looking at that laugh it doesn't look particularly sinister. How's this? AAAAA AAHHHHAAAAAA HHHAAAAA ... Any better? Probably not? Anyway what if we get wind of higher education later in life? What can you do then to stop us eh? Hmmmm. Cue sinister laugh again. HAR HA HAR ... no that's not it either - that sounds like a pirate. Oh I can't be bothered ... ha. I know! Don't help them. No, if we're over twenty-five and discover that it's useful to obtain knowledge then don't help us with grants and the like. Oh noooo! Let us struggle to pay for it ourselves. Make us pay for the education we should have received. Let us pay ...Whoops sorry got a tiny bit carried away there, back to the story.

Also at the ripe old age of sixteen my parents, much to my surprise, presented me with £500. They told me they'd opened a Prudential insurance account when I was born and had been saving each month. The reason they were saving? For my wedding! Bless their hearts. At sixteen they thought my main ambition in life was to get married. This concerned me on so many levels. The least of which was the fact in sixteen years the Pru had only given them a £500 quid payout. I couldn't bare it so I naturally said it was their money and I honestly had no intention of getting married anytime soon and gave it back to them.

I got a job in a well known bank, which I started the week after I finished school. I hated it with a passion and am rubbish with figures so all in all not the best choice for me. A few months later I wangled a secretarial job in a TV company which I bluffed as I had neither trained to be one nor ever heard of audio typing. Pun intended. The only downside to that job was that the guy I worked for had a set of teeth that the alien from the film Alien would have greatly admired.

At nineteen my boyfriend of four years (childhood sweetheart aahhh) and I bought a flat, thinking we'd be able to retire at forty and be mortgage free. What a plan for one so young. Boy did I have it sussed!

Then when I was twenty-one my father who was just fifty-nine was diagnosed with cancer. It never ceases to amaze me that I live in a country where about three weeks before my father passed away, I was on my way to work when I arrived at a massively over crowded station. It was heaving with people because no trains were running. Literally hundreds and hundreds of people would be late for work. Why? A poorly fox was lying on the tracks and everything was on hold until the RSPCA could come! Half an hour later the RSPCA turned up, climbed down on the track and put the poorly fox in a box. As they walked past me with it I asked them if it was ok (I think they totally missed my sarcastic tone) and the worried looking woman replied in all seriousness, "Not really, no. It's dying but at least we can make sure it dies peacefully". I think that's exactly what makes Great Britain truly grate.

Finally the week after Dad's initial collapse we had a name for his illness - "Acute Myeloid Leukaemia". My boyfriend and I got home around 10pm that day exhausted only to find we'd been burgled. The funny thing is I really did not care. Not a single tear was shed over it. I was too numb.

They'd taken everything. TV's, video, cameras, jewellery, the lot. Obviously we had to call the police. When they came I was so ashamed of the state of the flat e.g. washing and clothes everywhere. I did what any sloppy home keeper would do under the circumstances. I (to my boyfriend's utter amazement) unashamedly blamed "innocent" burglars for my own mess and slovenliness. Every cloud hey! I pointed at various pulled out draws and ransacked cupboards and lied through my teeth saying "see what they've done". Blaming burglars for the result of me being pushed to the limit with work, being at my Dad's bedside and too knackered to even contemplate housework. The only good memory from that night was my gorgeous friend Ginette and her partner Stuart coming straight over. I had to tell someone and I couldn't get my brothers or mother involved. They had enough to deal with without this. Ginette and Stu knocked on the door carrying with them the following: Their TV, their VHS, a huge sheet of chipboard (to board up the windows they'd smashed to gain entry) a bottle of wine and beers. THANK GOD FOR YOU X. Ironically, as we smashed out the remaining shards of the window, our neighbours suddenly developed a sense of hearing despite none of them seeing or hearing the burglars.

My father passed away when I was twenty-two. He was often hysterically funny without even realising it. When we challenged him about not taking his many and varied pills he would say "I'll take them when I feel better" and although it's completely Irish we all knew what he meant. Bless him. My Dad, my lovely Dad, who wore lavender or pink ruffled shirts right into the late eighties. He also loved jewellery. Believe me the Kardashians and P Diddy would have looked positively plain next to him! He was also quite artistic and made his own rings and belts and if he didn't make the things he wore he customised them. A great favourite was a leather fur lined flying jacket on the back of which he'd painted an eagle's head. We also had, throughout my childhood, a variety of cars (none of which left the drive on account of the fact they were heaps of junk) that he meticulously "hand painted" in a variety of pastel shades to suit his mood. Sometimes the odd eagle's head (he was good at those) or Viking appeared on their bonnets. He had a thing about Vikings, all things Egyptian, dinosaurs and armoury (as in guns, axes, swords etc.). In fact all along our beams at home we had enough (I hasten to add replica) guns, etc. to kit out the extras for many a battle sequence. Where was I? Oh yes, painting. When I first passed my driving test and purchased a car, I had to sit my Dad down the first time I went on holiday and make him cross his heart and promise that he wouldn't paint my car in my absence!

It was during the process of witnessing my father suffer a painful and prolonged death that I decided, well not so much decided as realised, that I had to change my entire life. After a couple of years worrying about how to escape my humdrum life without hurting my boyfriend, I summoned the courage to break the news. My incredible financial prowess meant that a flat we'd purchased for sixty thousand was now worth thirty. I eventually told my boyfriend (of ten years by this time), that I wanted to split. His reaction to this earth shattering news was "If that's what you want". No that wasn't what I wanted, I wanted him to tell me how stupid I was and how much he loved me and that I'd been through a hell of a time but with his support and love we'd be okay, we'd get through it. Actually his response was quite helpful as I now knew I was indeed making the right decision. Although I was expecting, rather vainly I suppose, more of a fight. I then decided it was time to make some sensible decisions so I moved back to my Mum's, sold everything I owned, left my job and trained to be an actor. "What? Are you mad?" I hear you cry. "That's a rubbish choice. There's no work and you'll be rejected daily". I knew all that but I'd always wanted to perform and the truth is I was painfully shy as a child and early adult and it took losing my father to make me realise you don't get a second chance.

During three years of training I officially boycotted men to concentrate solely on my work. I did however go out (platonically) with a total philanderer ex-colleague with whom I'd had a brief previous relationship. We did have a lot in common (not the philandering!). But I could never trust him. He did put on a good show of being a changed man and only wanting me and I was just starting to fall for it ... when out of the blue he phoned me to say that his ex-girlfriend (who, after splitting up with him, became a lesbian - something he seemed oddly proud of) was pregnant with his child! Boy I know how to pick 'em ... Tip for ex-girlfriends who wish to continue seeing their old boyfriends without raising the suspicions of their current girlfriend - immediately announce you are a raging lezzer. It fooled me completely.

Once I finished my training I got my old job back on a part-time basis, got my first agent and decided to be pro-active about meeting a significant other. So I persuaded two friends to go Speed Dating. What a great night. Out of twenty-five men there was only one who I liked and one other who wasn't bad looking but aloof and arrogant so I wrote "Psycho" in my notes and nothing else. In light of my good friend's notes on her dates, which included things like "nice aura" or "good shoes" my comment did seem a little harsh!

For some bizarre reason I actually went on dates with both of them - first with the one I liked and then with the "psycho" who actually on second look seemed to be okay. In fact I liked him. A lot. So much so that we ended up seeing each other regularly and eventually became boyfriend and girlfriend. Ah. We went on holiday together to the Maldives. He cut out the words "I love you" from a magazine and handed them to me on the plane! For Christmas he'd brought home some of the sand and shells from the Maldives beach and put them into clear glass candle stick holders. My friends were particularly impressed with that one! He asked me to move in with him. He was attentive and kind. Superb. Lucky me! Admittedly he could be a tad eccentric at times but I'm quite drawn to that. I blame my Dad. I've done it again, got side tracked. Sorry! I suppose what I was trying to say was that if the old adage is true that a girl always looks for a guy similar to her father then ... HELP!

* * * * *

Fast forward five months and I found myself living with the psycho and we were getting on well. I'd fallen in love hook, line and sinker. Then strange things started happening. We were cuddling on the sofa and I thought I felt him kiss the top of my head gently and thought "aahhhhh". However, when I moved I realised he hadn't kissed the top of my head, he had in fact thought it would be funny to stick his chewing gum on my head. As soon as I moved all my hair got stuck in it! Any girls reading this I guarantee will NOT find this amusing. I didn't find it funny in the slightest, especially when I looked in the mirror at the full horror. It was all stuck right at the top of my forehead and his "genius" suggestion was just to "cut it out". CUT IT OUT!! CUT IT OUT!? I would have been left with a mullet! It was a sign. I know. I should have left him then but I forgave him. Eventually.

Act of weirdness number two - I found out he had this strange thing about going to the toilet. Basically he could only go in places he knew. So could not use public toilets of any kind. Even weirder still was the fact that our first Valentine's weekend together he booked a weekend away in hotel - but not with me. No, he decided that out of the many other weekends available Valentine's weekend was the perfect time to spend it in a hotel with twenty other strange creatures who also couldn't wee in public toilets or in front of anyone! The format of their (let us not forget Valentine's) weekend included accompanying each other to public loos and weeing! Or alternatively pairing up with a similarly afflicted stranger to go to each other's hotel rooms and watch and/or listen to each other whilst weeing. As amusing as I suspect my disastrous love life is to you, dear reader, believe me I did not find it funny at the time. However, I relented a little when he explained that the guy who ran these sessions only ran them once a year. Mind you I think it's a little unfair running them on Valentine's weekend. Did this guy assume that these people have no partners because of this affliction? It's not that I hadn't and didn't try and support my partner with this. I had at his request stood outside our toilet door to see if he could go, knowing I was there. No luck though. I wonder now if in fact it wasn't all an elaborate lie. I do recall him telling me he broke his company laptop the previous year. How is this connected? Well he was stuck in traffic and bursting for a wee, so "he who cannot wee in public" tried to relieve himself into a mineral water bottle. Found he didn't have enough room so pushed the driver's seat back as far as it would go. Still not enough room so then he tilted the back of the seat all the way back to near horizontal. This gave him enough room to do the necessary but sadly his laptop was on the back seat and got crushed. Try explaining that one to your boss!

The last straw came - and I know I should have finished it there and then - when my nephew was seriously hurt in an accident. My nephew, who was nine at the time, had been running in the house and put his arm through the glass in the front door. Now had he put it through and left it the other side things would not have been so bad. But as is the natural reaction he pulled it straight back out and in the process severed a major artery and lost four pints of blood. I got that dreadful "now don't panic" phone call and when I told my boyfriend we needed to get to the hospital NOW! he said "Do I have to?" To which I naturally replied "Why wouldn't you want to?" He said, and I kid you not, "I'll be bored" ... Love is not only blind but incredibly stupid. I should have packed my bags and left for good immediately.

Obviously there were some good times but on the whole the bad outweighed the good. Nevertheless we decided to go on holiday to Spain to celebrate our second year together. The first week was fantastic. Sunshine, laughter and on the day of our anniversary he ran me a bath and put rose petals in it and lit candles. He'd also bought a variety of massage oils and gave me a full on pampering. He booked a fancy restaurant and we had a lovely meal out. It was great.

Then the next day I'd noticed that he'd been acting a little odd. You know? Furtive and nervous. For a fleeting moment I think oh ...my ... goodness, is he? He is! Could he be? Wow he is - he's going to propose. Oh shit. We've never spoken about marriage or children. We'd just been bumbling along. Like you do. So I try and play it cool. He pours me a glass of wine, sits me down, takes my hand, looks directly in my eyes and says: "I don't love you, I want you to move out and you should freeze your eggs".

GREAT! Bridget-fecking-Jones eat your heart out. Just when I thought I was about to merrily abseil off the shelf. TWANG. I find that I'm not abseiling after all. I am in fact bungee jumping. Shit.

So I replied "Well that's a huge shock", to which his super quick response was "The truth always hurts". WHAT? I was on to him now though so my recovery time decreased and I hit him straight back with "Well, that's all very well but who's going to tell the dog?" He quite clearly thought I'd gone mad. He was I think expecting a torrent of tears. He most certainly wasn't expecting a punchline.

We came back on day eight of a fourteen day holiday. I went back to work and he stayed at home. I tried to make sense of it all. Which was pretty useless as none of it made any sense at all. My head was spinning from wondering how long he'd not loved me? Had he been seeing someone else? Why didn't I see it coming? Then two days after we'd returned I come home from work and he actually smiles at me. Then he informs me "I think I may have over reacted - I've taken it down from Defcon Level 1 to Level 3". Naturally, I of course, looked bemused. Why was he now talking about our relationship in US Military defense terms? He continued "I've been reading this book (he lifts it so I can see. It's called 'Men are From Mars Women Are from Venus'). I think you should read it too". Hmmm the guy that had only a few days ago proposed in an extreme manner that I get out of his life, now wanted me to read a stupid arse relationship book. Then, just when you'd think it couldn't get any worse he presented me with ... wait for it ... three A4 handwritten pages of notes and informs me that it's a list of things he didn't like about me. UNF***KING BELIEVABLE. Points included:

1) **I swear.** And in brackets he had put **("I know I do a lot but that's ok")**. No comment.

2) **The towels smell funny** - "Yeah that's right, sweetie, that unusual smell you didn't recognize was LENOR".

3) **Our families could never meet** - Let me translate: You Jo are from a council estate and working class. I grew up in a chocolate box village and my parents are incredibly posh.

4) **I burp** - Call the police, it's true! I also pass wind although that went unmentioned.

5) **I say "Do you know what I mean" too much and tilt my head** - I do, it's true so be warned any girlfriends out there. This simple phrase and action could leave you sitting home alone with only your frozen eggs for company.

6) **He didn't like any of my friends** - Apologies to all my friends, but it wasn't until we split that they all let loose on exactly how they felt about him. They all miss him terribly and send their love!

In retrospect I suppose it's to be expected. Speed dating cost £20 and I met twenty-five men so it works out that I paid approximately 80p per bloke. The saying "you get what you pay for" springs to mind. I should, I suppose, consider myself lucky that the three pages were single sided! It was bound to fail: he clearly thought he was living with Vicky Pollard while I stupidly thought I was living with an adult.

* * * * *

The Break Up De-humourised:

It hit me unbelievably hard. In fact it completely knocked the wind out of me. I was crushed. To top it all he wanted me to move out of his house the weekend we got back. I had nowhere to go. Well, all my friends said I could crash at theirs but I needed somewhere more private than a friend's sofa. On our first evening back I phoned a close male friend that lived just down the road who rescued me and refused to let me go back that night so I stayed with him and his flat mate. I then found out about a house available to rent. So I stayed at friends the next couple of days and waited to move out. When I got back to his flat to pack my things up I was distraught to find that he'd put all my belongings into black bin bags. On closer inspection he hadn't "put" them in, he had literally tipped the contents of various drawers in to bags. It was awful. I was too upset to even say anything. The day of the move I had a convoy of friends' cars taking my stuff to my new house. To round off a shitty week, two hundred yards from my new house a car came whizzing round a blind bend and crashed straight in to me. As I've said previously, when something hugely shite is going on in your life it is in fact quite a good time for one of the annoying but less shite things to happen. Because you just don't care. Christmas was just round the corner too so the timing was impeccable. My Dad had passed away around Christmas time so the run up to Christmas and the whole celebration has taken years to claim back. Just when you think you're on top of things life strikes you with another resounding kick in the groin.

I decided there and then that I would spend Christmas Eve and Christmas Day helping people that have a shit time the whole time and help them have at least a few easy or easier days. I signed up with Crisis and spent those two days in their Deptford Centre being extremely humbled. It was the best thing I could have done and also one of the best Christmases I've ever had before or since. Oddly I found that the majority of homeless people, in fact probably 95%, were guys and that conversely around 95% of the volunteers were women. Over the two days of chatting with both the other volunteers and the homeless I began to make a strange discovery. Almost all of the homeless guys there ended up on the streets because they'd lost their wives, children, their jobs or someone they loved. The stories were harrowing. On the other hand again almost every volunteer I spoke to was going through the loss of their husband, a divorce or in some cases after a messy divorce this was their first Christmas day without their children. I found it interesting that both the homeless and the volunteers were essentially there for the same reasons. Both were just dealing with them in very different ways.

* * * * *

Fast forward a week and I'm living beyond my means alone in a rented house. I'm persuaded to go to a singles party. I think "Oh well why not?" I'll tell you why not! I hate clubs at the best of times owing to their general meat market atmosphere. So why, oh why, did I have a weak moment and agree to attend a club filled with wall-to-wall desperados? I hated it. I loathed it. I wanted to go home ... Right up until I met quite a nice bloke ... Yes it's true! We got talking, he was tall, very smiley, single and with all his own teeth as far as I could tell! To top it all we even shared a cab home as he lived just down the road! BINGO! There is a God. He takes my number (the smiley bloke, not God) and we say goodnight and I'm happy as Larry.

He calls me and we go out. He seems rather lovely. He's not long split form his girlfriend too so we both know we're a little bruised. After a couple of weeks he asks me to be, ah bless him, "his girlfriend" to which I agree. So I officially have a boyfriend again. We sleep together for the first time. It is no great shakes but then it never is with someone new. Regardless, my heart is singing at the thought of being wanted. Then what does he do next? Nothing. He doesn't call me that evening despite saying he would. So I call him and leave a message. Next day - still no reply to message. So I leave it, reasoning he must have lost his phone or something. Yeah right! Another day goes by. I leave another message - this time, I have to admit, really quite an angry one as I now feel like the "girlfriend" bit was a "get her in the sack" line. After four days I get a phone call saying that he needed some "time" as he cleared out all his girlfriend's stuff from his flat and it hit him harder than he thought it would. He asked me out to dinner. At dinner I told him exactly how his actions had made me feel and he seemed genuinely sorry that I'd been upset. He said he really liked me and would need a little time. I agreed we both needed to take things slowly but that he had to let me know if he needed space to think, not just leave me high and dry. So we continued to see each other for about another month.

One evening we were on our way to the cinema, he'd picked me up and we were going to pick up his friend when his mobile rings. He answers and says he's on the way to the cinema with Dave. Dave is clearly not even in the car. I however clearly am. He finishes his conversation then turns and tells me it was his girlfriend. Like I didn't already know that! I asked him why he lied and he said she was already crying and he didn't want to upset her further! We went to movies to see "Closer" which is possibly THE worst film to see whilst in the middle of a relationship crisis. He dropped his mate off first then me and said nothing more. I, of course, festered all night about my presence being denied and going out with a bloke who considered his ex-girlfriend's feelings more important than his current girlfriend's. So I wrote him a stinking email expressing just that. He rang me later that evening. I was of course expecting an apology. But oh no. He said "it was fine, it's over" and that he'd only ever planned on seeing me "twice a week" anyway. TWICE A FECKING WEEK? What am I? Some kind of yoga class? I pointed out that since we'd met he'd seen me about four times every week so did that mean he got two months off entirely!!!! SOMEONE PLEASE TELL ME WHY I AM ATTRACTED TO THESE MEN? Needless to say I never saw him again. During all this time I'm getting more and more in debt as I can't afford to rent a house alone.

The answer to my financial problems arrived briefly in the form of a friend (the "nice aura" girl who went speed dating with me). She'd also recently crashed her car. How? She was listening to her meditation tape whilst driving! I pointed out (rather unnecessarily) the dangers of this. However she insisted it was the only chance in her busy life she had to listen to it. So she moved in and shared the house with me. All was going well until eight months later she gets fired and moves out. I decide the only way I can get financially straight is, yes, you guessed it, GO BACK HOME - AGAIN.   NNNOOOOOOOOOOOOOOOO.

So there it is. I'm living with my mother, with no lucrative acting jobs, a part-time job I loathe, in debt and with no boyfriend. But I do have a plan. I intend to save enough in the next year for a deposit on my own house. I created my own website too. Check it out: www.joburke.com

Did you look at it? See? I am an actor. And I can act. So if any *Eastenders*, scriptwriters, directors or producers are reading this you know what to do. If I had a pound for every time someone has told to me I should be in *Eastenders* well, well I'd have at least a fiver ... Hmmmm ... I should point out that I would of, course, never turn down a role in *Eastenders* however I do consider myself of a higher pedigree. I see myself more as a young Julie Walters, Jen Saunders or Catherine Tate. I'd actually really prefer to have my own series. However, it's been a struggle trying to get anyone interested when you have no literary agent and you can't get a literary agent to take you until you've been published! It's the same miserable catch-22 you have as an actor. I will persevere. As my brother says, "Cream always rises to the top". Mind you, saying that, I had thought I'd be a well-known actor by now and my face would be on the cover of magazines like "Vogue" and "FHM". Instead, sadly, casting directors seem to have seen through my attempts to rise to the top. To date I have been the face of, wait for it, "Oxfam" and "Family Tax Credit". Who am I trying to kid? Where was I? Oh yes! I'll need a lodger again but at least I'll be putting up with sharing in order to pay MY mortgage and I won't just be lining a landlord's pocket. Now I need to address my neglected love life. Speed dating for some reason doesn't appeal. So what's left?

"Everyone does it these days"

"It's nothing to be ashamed of"

"You never know"

"Nothing ventured"

"One of them offers a free six months if you don't meet someone in the first six months"

"My sister in law's brother's goat met his wife on the net"

"Make love happen"

Right. Come on get pro-active. You've realised that Mr Tall, Dark, Handsome and most importantly SANE won't simply knock on your door. In fact the only blokes knocking at your door are the pizza delivery guy, gas man and your sixty-six year old mother's stream of suitors. What do you do? There's only one thing for it. We're living in the 21st Century after all so what am I waiting for? What's the worst that could happen? Well everyone I know could see my photo and assume, possibly correctly, that I'm a pathetic, desperate and lonely individual. Ah, but anyone who sees my photo would also be a member so how could THEY criticise? Oh no! What if any old boyfriends are on there? Or my boss? Or worse, my mum? I think it's safe to say my mum won't be on there as she's still mastering the microwave. I suppose it could be worse. You could find your current husband/boyfriend or wife/girlfriend on there. I wonder if that's ever happened? Hmmmm. Hang on, you can't find your current partner on there unless you are also cheating. In which case it would simply serve you right would it not? *Stop it.* What? *Thinking too much.* I always over analyse everything. It's a nightmare. Why can't I just get on with things without that damn parrot on my shoulder giving me a million reasons why not to? Sod it Polly.

Even the toilets are 100%
behind my decision

Awesome April

Here it goes:

Jo's Profile:

Name: **Jo**

Age: **33**

About Jo:

Family Status: **Single**

Sexuality: **Straight**

Children: **Zero**

Education: **College**

Profession: **Other**

Religion: **None**

Employment: **Employed**

Practising (religion): **Non Practising**

Income: **Moderate**

Star Sign: **Taurus**

Race: **Caucasian / White**

Eye Colour: **Blue**

Height: **5'1" - 5'4" (1.51m - 1.60m)**

Hair Colour: **Dark Brown**

Build: **Average / Medium**

Hair Length: **Long**

Appearance: **Attractive**

Smoker: **None**

Drinker: **Light**

Vegetarian: **No**

Interests: **Pop / Classical / Jazz Music, Movies, Theatre, Dancing, Animals, The Arts, Restaurants, Pubs / Clubs, Reading, TV / Radio**

More about Jo and what she is looking for:

I enjoy comedy - both stand up and TV - favourites are Little Britain, Nighty Night, The Office, League of Gentlemen etc. I decided a few years back that life was too short to work five days a week. I wanted to spend more time doing things I enjoy. So I now work three days a week and spend the other days either writing, walking the dog, going to the gym or going to castings as I'm also a struggling actor, hence you not recognising me and me being on this site! I'm 5'3, loyal, loving, considerate, optimistic and enjoy socialising and meeting new people. I guess I am simply looking for someone who understands what is important in life who is not a procrastinator, someone with a spark and who is not afraid or feels it's a weakness to show their emotions. Would be lovely if they were caring, tall (6ft) with gorgeous eyes and a full head of hair! No players need apply - you know who you are!

Jo is looking for someone...

Age: **30 to 45**

Looking For: **A Serious Relationship**

Race: **Any**

Religion: **Any**

Children: **No**

Smoker: **No**

Blimey that was easy! I'm now on-line dating! Get me. Can't wait to see who will respond. There must be someone out there on the other end of a laptop with my name on it? In the meantime I'm jotting down my thoughts as to how you can spot the early signs that you are - how shall I say? - approaching your "Sell-By" date.

Ten tell tale signs you could be passed or nearing your Sell-By date:

1. You often squeeze into a dress size too small in changing rooms and get stuck or have come close to having to ask for assistance getting out of a garment or have thought about just ripping it off.

2. You admit and now buy the correct shoe size. I am and always have been a size six. However I always think the next size down looks better and previously always squished my feet into a five!

3. You not only find yourself wanting to write stiff letters for bad service etc. but even worse actually write and post complaints.

4. You notice how rude the "youth of today" are.

5. At a party you meet a soldier and you think he looks like a ten year-old boy in fancy dress.

6. You now take cod liver oil tablets.

7. You'd consider botox if it wasn't so expensive and didn't involve needles in your face.

8. Your mother borrows your clothes!

9. It takes six months of yoga, four times a week, for you to be able to touch your toes and if you miss a week it takes another six months before you can do it again.

10. When you say you are going to "stretch your legs" you actually mean pop up to bed for a lay down.

And so it begins …

Message From David:

Hi Jo,

I just wanted to say that I think you sound FANTASTIC and you look INCREDIBLE too, I would love to have a chat and get to know you so why don't you get back and tell everything about yourself, what do you like doing in your spare time stuff like that, well me,, I like to live life to the full, there isn't enough hours in the day for me and I"ll give anything ago once and if I like it I'll do it again and if I don't then I won't. well you take care and I really do hope to speak to you very soon. here's a very BIG SMILE just for you. mark. XxX

Well so far so good - not bad for a first response. Am I being too fussy? I don't feel inclined to "tell everything". Let's see who else has spotted me:

Message From Zav:

Hi Jo,

I saw your advert.And I must admit that you look fantastic.Please tell me more about yourself

regards Zav

Wow. Two "fantastics" in the first two emails! He also wants to know more! Sadly he doesn't have a photo attached. His full name is **Zdvrikz** which I simply cannot pronounce hence any further discussion would seem futile. Also I don't like his insinuating I'm advertising myself in the manner of a car in Loot.

Message From John:

Hi Jo,

Am kingsley by name, i was fortunate to have come accross your profile whi i find stunning enough and your profile which makes me get attracted to you. Please if you dont mind , i d love to be a firend, tell me NO PROBS!!! And am gonna be the HAPPIEST GUY in the WORLD,ok. Pleaseee. REPLY BACK TO ME TO THIS EMAIL It's gonna be my pleasure to see your LOVELY MAIL in my pretty box,ok.

Thanks.

OK. Now what is his first name? John as in "Message from John" or Kingsley as in "Am Kingsley by name"? Can you be "Kingsley" by nature? Afraid there will be none of my "LOVELY MAIL in his pretty box". No photo and lives in Lagos ... NEXT ... Oh hang on, I suppose I should just look at his profile. It's a tad shallow to not see what the guy is about just because he's not added a photo, don't you think?

About John:

Family Status: **Single**

Sexuality: **Straight**

Children: **Zero**

Education: **University**

Profession: **Other**

Religion: **Christian**

Employment: **Student**

Practising (religion): **Occasional**

Income: **Low**

Star Sign: **Cancer**

Race: **Black / African descent**

Eye Colour: **Black**

Height: **6'5" - 6'8" (1.91m - 2.00m)**

Hair Colour: **Black**

Build: **Average / Medium**

Hair Length: **Short**

Appearance: **Attractive**

Facial Hair: **Clean Shaven**

Smoker: **None**

Drinker: **Light**

Vegetarian: **No**

Interests: **Movies**

More about John and what he is looking for:

MY NAMES ARE JOHN NAPOLEON LIKE YOUY ALREADY KNOW. I AM FROM EDO STATE AND I RESIDE IN LAGOS. I AM A STUDENT AND I ALSO WORK IN A CYBER CAFE. I AM THE FIRST OF SIX CHILDREN. I AM

A COOL AND EASY GOING PERSON. I AM LOOKING FOR SOME REALLY COOL, NICE, LOVELY AND HONEST GIRL FOR A SERIOUS RELATIONSHIP.

John is looking for someone...

Aged: **18 to 25**

Looking For: **A Serious Relationship**

Race: **Black / African descent**

Religion: **None**

Children: **No**

Smoker: **No**

How many damn names can one guy have? 6'5 to 6'8 - I know I said tall but that's simply ridiculous. I apologise to all the perfectly happy giants out there but I am after all a mere 5'4" (Yes, I realise 'More about Jo' said 5'3" ... I don't know why, I lied). John, Napoleon, Kingsley, whatever is clearly also blind as I am, I would say, obviously not of Black/African descent nor 18 to 25 ...

Message From Lucian:

Ciao Jo, how are you?

I like your profile. What do you think of mine?

If you want to find out a bit more about me get in touch... From tomorrow, 8 Jan, I'll only be available on my personal email as my 3 days trial is due to expire today 7 Jan...

Luca, the Italian ;-)

Ooohhh an Italian. Tall. His profile says 6"1. Unfortunately he describes his hair as short, which is rather cunning. In fact his photo proves he's as bald as a Badger. Badgers aren't bald are they? Why do we say that? Anyway I have a pet hate for adults, male or female, who insist on using smiling/winking faces throughout their emails. Don't even get me started on abbreviations LOL!

ARRRRRRGGGHHHHHHHHHHHHHHHHH. Luca is also not a big spender or serious about finding a significant other. Three day trial I ask you ...

Message From Demitri:

Hi Jo,

your descripion impressed me. You must have a very interesting personality.

Oh my God. This man is truly terrifying. I wish you could see him. Here's his profile:

More about Demitri and what he is looking for:

I am very nice person. with specyfic sense of humor. I am interested in music, films, coputers and psychology. I would like to meet nice woman , who will fail in love with me. I live in london since 2004 and I dont know much people there.

Quite scary that he managed to spell "psychology" correctly in a sea of spelling errors. I'm a little concerned that the only reason he can spell "psychology" is because the word hangs above the door of his ward. Ahh bless him. Sadly I have little or no interest in "Coputers" and at this stage in the game it's my honest opinion that I will not be falling in love with him. I can confirm that I will at his own suggestion "fail" to love him. On another note, Demitri, you've been living here for two years now you MUST know some people by now?

Message From Andre:

Jo....you are very beautiful........

how are you doing? My name is Sandy, I saw your photo and I must say that you are really nice! I don't believe a lot in these web sites.....what we were supposed to say here......if we haven't never met before....I believe that eyes contact, smile, the way you make a sentence, the time you spend with a person and what you feel you have in common with are more important than photos, jobs and favourites dishes.....actually, I am more interested in someone who is not like me and therefore can move my brain and show me things in a different way!!!

Honestly.....the way you look in that photo is gorgeous......and saying that I think that I would love to move from this kind of conversation......and hear the sound of your voice.....

Sandy

He's a bit forward. Not my cup of tea in the looks department either. I'm devastated to learn that if I emailed to tell him a cereal bowl is my favourite dish he would not be impressed. I also think he has more faith in my abilities than I do. I mean even Uri Geller can't move brains. Oh lets see what his profile says anyway ...

More about Andre and what he is looking for:

So what do you wanna know? I work hard, play harder and think life is for living, not enduring. I love holidays and like to go away as often as possible. Wanna know what I look like? 6' 2", slim,

dark hair and ayes, beautiful eyelashes, Mediterranean. Just gorgeous really..... oh, and I'm modest too! What do I like to do? I enjoy cinema, theatre, socialising, travelling (a lot.....)and pretty much anything that involves getting out and about and meeting people

If only I was drawn to a gentleman's eyelashes. We could have shared something special. What's with the name thing? Message from Andre and he signs off Sandy?

Message From Dean:

Hi Jo,

Thought I would drop you a note to say Hi. So,..Hi. Hope this year is treating you well and not all of your resolutions have gone out the window (my January no alcohol resolution went the first weekend!) .

Really liked your profile and would love to find out more about you. Me, I am very simple (not in the head or anything), uncomplicated, funny (I know everybody says that and thinks they are but I will leave that up to you to decide), honest, caring, reliable, fit (in the gym sense), nice blue eyes and lots of hair (on my head!).

Drop me a line if you would like to chat or know more. Take care

Dean x

At last a normal chap. Hoooo-bloody-ray. I might reply to him. Doesn't look too bad either. Shall I reply? I'll think about it ...

* * * * *

I know it's been a while but here it goes ...

Message Sent To Dean:

Hi Dean,

Apologies for the delay.

Thanks for the lovely message so far so good how about you?

How are you finding internet dating?

Jo

OK so it took me a few weeks - I've been busy. He's not replied. Perhaps he's on holiday, or just busy working, or not on the site anymore. Damn it I shouldn't have left it so long...

Message From Pete:

Hi Jo,

How are you?

I'm Not a Player!!!

It surprises me when I see someone as beautiful as you, on a site like this!!

Amazing!! I would think you could have your pick of men! But I guess not.

You have a fantastic smile, and I thought I would say "Hi".

I guess the rest is up to you!

Take care, Pete x

"But I guess not". Is he taking the piss? What's he trying to imply? That I can't get a boyfriend? Curses on these sites - you can't appear nonchalant and aloof if you're blatantly advertising yourself to all and sundry. I'm not sure I like this at all ... I'd have a better response if I was a clapped out Volkswagen.

Message From Rick:

Hi Jo, I have read what u have said about yrself and u sound like a nice person if u want to get hold of me? Maybe we can have a chat Maybe speak to u later.

Well I think you can guess that I wouldn't be remotely interested in "getting hold of" someone who can't be bothered to type up correctly long words like "you". I know ... I know you're now thinking you know why I'm still single. I stand by my principles, despite your knowing nods. Besides, he's balding and lives too far away. Oh for Christ's sake stop it! I know I know ... leave me alone!

Message From Derek:

Hi Jo,

My name is Derek and I live and work in Croydon.

I work as a civil servant for the CPS, which has it's moments, but is mostly just paperwork and not as exciting as you may think.

I live in my own house with a cat called Tabitha.

In my spare time I am a member of a local theatre group. I also like to read, watch TV, go to the theatre and the cinema and to go out to eat and drink (not necessarily in that order).

I enjoy cooking, especially big meals for lots of people, but I can do romantic dinners for two as well.

I like the countryside, particularly the remote wild places. In the summer I enjoy visiting village pubs for a pint and a ploughman's.

I am quite well travelled. I have been to the USA, Canada, Peru, Norway, Iceland, Morocco, Nepal, Indonesia and Europe. My travels have been closer to home since I got a mortgage.

I enjoy going out, but miss having someone to go out with. I would love to hear from you.

Derek.

How could I go on a date with a man who presumes I'd think working as a Civil Servant might be exciting? Don't even get me started on Tabitha ... more about Derek:

More about Derek and what he is looking for:

I am quiet, easy going and patient. I enjoy going to the cinema and theatre and going out for a drink or to eat. I'm well read, well traveled and a good cook. I enjoy the countryside espcially the remote, wild places.

Derek enjoys remote wild places - I bet he does. Somewhere quiet where he'll tie you up, rob and murder you and the police will use the photo from this site on the news!

Message From Kalvin:

Hi Jo,

wow you look fantastic.....

That's all he put. The dots may lead you to believe there was more but nope he felt that was sufficient.

It's all very flattering. That's what you're thinking, aren't you? Receiving complimentary emails? Well let me tell you it would be flattering if every one of the guys that sent them didn't resemble Andrew Lloyd Webber on a particularly bad day after having disastrous plastic surgery. What part of my profile, which I should remind you, states: "with a full head of hair" does nobody understand?

Message From Dave:

Hi Jo,

Oh come on Jo. Bald can be sexy too! Dave

Can they mind read now? What's happening? Baldies everywhere - be gone. It's not my fault I'm simply not, and have never been, attracted to the follically challenged. Or short men for that matter. It's genetic I'm sure so please don't blame me.

Message From Christian:

Hi Jo,i know i dont fit what ur lookin for but had to say that you have a very lovely smile and captivating eye's. all the best.

Oh what's the point? Yes he is bald ... as well as the typ ... oh I'm losing the will to live.

Right, let's check my 'normal' inbox...

Ah, I have an audition. Zippidee doo dah day there is a God!

Hi Jo,

Here are the details for your appointment. Further details below.

Good Luck

PROJECT: (Music Video) Production: Bingo Wings

PART: Female Models

OTHER INFO:

We are looking for FEMALE plus size models 14/16+ for Music Video.

'Bingo Wings' by new UK band. All auditionees must move well. Girls must be confident with their size and be willing to shake it on the dance floor.

Agreements / Contracts / Fees: Unfortunately there is no fee attached to the project but travel expenses & refreshments will be provided. Big names such as Christopher Biggins already on board.

Arrgghhhhhhhhhhhhhhhhhhhhhhhhhhhhhhhhh! What's going on? I am a size 10 NOT a size 16 and I do not have BINGO FECKING WINGS. To add even more insult to injury I'd be expected to gain two dress sizes overnight and flaunt my newly acquired flab for the grand sum of NOTHING, NADA, ZIP. Of which I should point out my excellent agent should receive 20%. You know it's time to get a new agent when their idea of a "big name" is none other than CHRISTOPHER BIGGINS ... I am speechless. "Change your agent" you may be thinking. It's not that simple - you have no idea how long it's taken me to even find a rubbish one. Nevertheless when you're down there's only one place left to go.

Either I have a speech impediment
or I stole someone called Ray's
coffee this morning

May Madness

Message From Nathan:

Hi Jo,

Without going into too much boring detail about myself here's a little rundown...

6ft1

Scottish

Naughty cheeky boy

30

Live music and sport fan

Like theatre and cinema

Travel a lot..

Work in television

Live in Wimbledon

Drive a car

Have two legs both working.

Can cook

Can operate a washing machine. Like pets

Look good in a kilt.

Can speak Mandarin!!!

Have been up kilimangiro...

Anyway that's it.

Get in touch.

There's a money back guarantee

Oh yes and the photo is crap I am trying to change it.. I do have hair and a chin.

Nathan

He may well have gone to enormous trouble in climbing up a huge mountain but he certainly didn't spare any time on his way up to read any signposts in order to help him spell it. Other than that though it's excellent - just what I needed. Direct, funny and interesting. I shall respond accordingly ... I won't dilly-dally this time either.

Message Sent To Nathan:

Hi Nathan,

Hey loved your breakdown. Superb!

Me: 5ft 2 and a bit nearly 3

English

Sharp wit often sarcastic 33

Stand up/live comedy Theatre/Film

Travel Germany/Vienna/Italy last year Work in IT part time

Live South East London

Drive a car too

Two legs check working check

Born defroster

Can operate one but it only leads to ironing! Have a dog

Haven't worn a kilt since school

Ate a Mandarin today

Impressive

Afraid my chin and hair are both false. I think it's best to be completely honest at this stage!

Jo

What do you think? I'm happy with it. Let's see how it goes. For the first time this feels like fun.

Message From Nathan:

Ello Jo. Great to hear from you. Nice pic.

I am from a family of actors so know how tough it is out there.. but don't despair. I really do love the theatre and try to get out as much as possible.

I love comedy and try to get to Jongleurs in Battersea about once a month. My friend Sarah has also trained to be a stand-up so try and get to see her in action too.

Glad that your chin and hair are both false.. my hair is removable like those lego men!

I'll forgive the missing "H". He seems like a nice chap although I'd prefer to be able to see the hair situation. The chin I am happy to believe IS actually there. Now my next slight reservation would be Who the fuck is Sarah? I know they're "friends" but why does he feel the need to mention her to me now? I too am a girl that has male "friends". I know for certain I don't want to have sex with any of them. But the real question is: do they want to with me? How can I ever know? I can't be sure. I'm rubbish. How can I possibly have a pang of jealousy about the friend I've never met, of a man I've never met? I could email back:

"What's the story with Sarah then - pretty is she? Slept with her have you? We haven't even met and you're referring to other females. Stop wasting my time and shag her if you haven't already.

Take care Jo"

That, I feel, is neither positive nor progressive, so I think I shall opt for:

Message Sent To Nathan:

Hi Nathan,

I have a couple of friends dabbling on the stand up scene. It's not something I could do. It's harsh! Where did she train? I shall cease any further contact until I receive photographic confirmation of your follicles!

Jo

I do really have some stand up comedy friends so I'm not just trying to top him. I also thought it was a stroke of genius enquiring after "Sarah's" training although in my deepest most evil depths the only thing "trains" and "Sarah" have in common is that she goes like one! Okay, I own up. I'm not that bitter and twisted - it's a joke. However should she keep coming up I will have serious questions to ask Nathan.

Message From Nathan:

Hi Jo,

Well that'll have to be sent via email.. She is training at a place in London I can't remember the name of it....

I can text you a better pic!!!

Nathan.

Phew Sarah has reverted to a "she" and if he can't remember where she's training that to my mind means one of two things: 1) He doesn't think enough of her to bother remembering or 2) He doesn't really listen to anyone. I see he's trying to bribe me into giving him my mobile number and email address. Basically if I want to see a decent picture I have to divulge my personal information.

Message Sent To Nathan:

Hi Nathan,

I expect she's training at City Lit. I looked into the stand up thing and they do courses and a friend of mine did his there.

My mobile number is XXX and email is XXX blimey now you know all my contact details! You're a fast worker!

Jo

See, I told you I wasn't lying about my stand up friends, and I listen! Don't know what came over me but for some reason I felt fine handing over my contact details and at least I'll get confirmation that he does have a chin and a lid on his head.

Nathan sent me an MMS of exactly the same (e.g. no chin no top of head) photo as he has on the dating site. This in my opinion is getting extremely fishy. I am now of course convinced he is a bald, or worse, GINGER dwarf with a chin that resembles an outsized arse. He tells me he "looks better in the flesh". Again, is this blackmailing me into an actual - dare I say it, or even think it - *meeting*? This is not as straightforward as I thought.

Message From Roberto:

Hi Jo,

Read your profile so thought I would say hi. About Me! Exercise is my balance, music my passion, laughter my preference, humor my soft spot, traveling my fun, friends my joy, love my purpose, You my date? I would love to find out more about you!

I Hope to hear from you soon.   Robertox

Someone always has to go and spoil it for everyone ... pass the sick bag ... signed Robertox more like bollox Roberto.

Message From James:

Hi Jo,

Did you receive my message?

In the meantime, here's another internet dating dilemma. No, James, I did not receive your message. However, sadly, you've attached a photo that I think would be better suited in a gallery of nerds or possibly kiddy fiddlers. Not only that, you clearly don't know who you have and haven't sent messages to.

This does however raise an important question. What is the internet dating etiquette for situations when you receive emails from people with whom you have no wish to communicate? I have, as is obvious, simply been finding them hilarious and ignoring them. It strikes me now, though, that ignoring them may be a tad unsympathetic. The only other option though, is to hurt their feelings by replying and spelling out that I'm not interested. Is it better to ignore or be brutally honest? Also, with the scales tipping the balance in favour of the ones I'm not interested in, replying to them would actually involve the majority of my time being spent emailing people I don't like. It's a modern moral dilemma. Also, I bet if you did phrase the rejection email in a kind gentle manner they'd be so grateful that they'd email back. And then where does that leave you? In a worse position than before, as now they think you're even nicer than they first thought! This is a nightmare.

SINGLES LOG: DATE NUMBER ONE

Preliminary emails: Basic and to the point so cut to the chase and arranged to meet The South African

We agree to meet in a pub just outside Waterloo. I arrive on time which is actually late for me. Don't know why I'm obsessive about being on time, maybe it's because I consider it outrageous to arrange a time to meet someone and not have the respect and good manners to be there. Or maybe it's the actor in me ... the earlier you are, the more time to prepare. Who knows? I digress. I think I've already spotted him at a table and my heart has already sunk. He looks nowhere near as attractive as his photo. He's wearing thick-rimmed large glasses (navy blue!) and is sporting an anorak. Again I have an etiquette issue. Do I honestly say to the guy "Sorry to have bothered you but I could in fact have you arrested under the Trades Description Act. Good day to you, Sir"? Of course I can't. So, what do I do? I take a seat opposite him and chat. He does offer to get me a drink but his glass is still almost full and I already feel guilty so nip to the bar to get my own.

Although I'm not attracted to him in the slightest he does have some redeeming features. He's intelligent and well read. Perhaps a less shallow person would be able to see past the visual package. I give myself a two drink limit and hope he understands and can read between the lines. He gets up to visit the little boy's room and I'm stunned to see as he walks away that he has an extremely pronounced limp. I look up to the yellowed, peeling and cracked ceiling and ask God "*Why me?*" Of course, God doesn't reply, and if he did I'm sure He'd shout "Why you? You selfish cow - *he's* the one with the limp you obnoxious atheist". I am indeed an atheist and selfish so I appreciate I really shouldn't be wasting his time. I bet He's up there wetting his pants/toga type thing at how hypocritical all us Atheists & Agnostics are from time to time. I'm sure we all do it: raise our eyes to the God(s)/ceiling or light fitting and ask "WHY?" My date returns, limping back towards me. He sits down and explains that he has cerebral palsy. Naturally, I now feel even more guilty and the conversation becomes a little, shall we say, stilted. I hope with all my heart that he'd picked up on the fact that there wasn't any spark initially. No mutual attraction prior to his visit to the loo.

I realise it must be a difficult situation for him. But I really do feel that it's important to be up front and honest in all areas of life and especially with something on that scale. I can see his dilemma. If he mentions it before will anyone agree to a date? I'm sure my answer would have been no. So maybe he's right to let people find out on a date. He's not technically lying is he? I mean he at no point said he didn't have cerebral palsy.

You hate me now don't you? Be honest. I get it. You're thinking "Now come on you selfish cow (echoing God's admonishment) this guy has cerebral palsy and you're more concerned about dating". I hope you will have noticed by now that I use humour in awkward situations and going on a blind date with a disabled person would be, shall we say, difficult enough if you had prior knowledge. However being thrown into this situation unwittingly is even worse. Can you honestly say, hand on heart, when you were or if you are looking for a partner - you know, the guy you wanted to marry, have children with get old with - Can you honestly say that the image of this partner has a limp? I'm not for one moment saying that, had there been a mutual attraction between us, a limp would have been a deal breaker, not at all. Although I'm not foolish enough to say that it wouldn't have been an issue for me. There would be important questions if I intended to have a relationship with this guy like: "Is it hereditary?" etc.

Not a great start ... *It's all about you isn't it?* What now? *You. You. You. Did you ever consider that maybe the date went like this?:*

Guy turns up early at pub gets himself a beer settles down with eager anticipation. Girl turns up. His heart sinks. She's nothing like her photo. She's thinner than she looked. (He has a soft spot for the cuddly type - she also has a chest you could do your ironing on.) It's a devastating blow. He's disappointed but tries to hide it. He offers her a drink but she decides to get her own as his is almost full. He's quite impressed by that. She returns from the bar and they chat. As the conversation develops he realises that she bores the pants off him and notices she's wearing too much make up. "Why do women do that?" he wonders as he stares despondently into his beer. She continues to talk at him with little or no let up. It's clear to him that she fancies him. He's almost involuntarily hatching plans to abort. What can he do to escape? He runs through various scenarios as her blood red lips continue to move unrelentingly. "Excuse me" he interrupts gingerly "I just need to visit the toilet". Before he knows it, Kevin Spacey like a la The Usual Suspects, he starts to walk away with a pronounced limp ... cut to a dinner party years later with his friends ..."So what's the most evil thing you've ever done?" He searches his memory, his face goes crimson, then he announces "I once, and I am not proud of this ... pretended to have cerebral palsy in order to get out of an absolutely horrendous date." Impressed gasps prevail from the males in the room whilst the women look horrified.

Three sides to every story: Your side, their side and the truth. OH! Leave me alone.

It's a Jungle out there June

More about James and what he is looking for:

Young at heart Leo male looking to meet a woman who can be fun,tactile and loves to laugh but not always at me!I am caring,loving man with a good sence of humour(northern), friendship leading to Romance long term but frindship good, first.I like the arts,antiques,classic cars, music,Bolton football, seaside, comedy nights,carboots,all the normal stuff,looking after my 13y special needs son takes up some time with work the other,J 11 M25, hence doing this!I like pubs,clubs,enjoy a bottle of red and my home cinema,done many things.. a house-husband,main carer,salesman...now single, I am well trained and would like to travel more happy in all company..try me out!!

Now this is another James. He resembles a 1950's news reader and is 46. I know along with the rest of the nation I shouldn't be so hung up on looks. But the truth is, you do have to be physically attracted to someone. So don't be too harsh on me for being honest. I do, however, feel that this James has the "aaahhh" factor. Which I'm sure he would hate. He doesn't want pity - he wants to meet the woman of his dreams. I'm tempted to reply *"Congratulations James you are a winner! Please accept this email as recognition for the 'Worst Spelt and Grammatically Incorrect email ever Sent."* I think he should strongly consider a visit to the opticians, as his Dame Edna style spectacles appear to need a lens update.

About James:

Family Status: **Separated**

Sexuality: **Straight**

Children: **1**

Education: **University of Life**

Profession: **Sales & Marketing**

Religion: **None**

Employment: **Employed**

Practising (religion): **Non Practising**

Income: **Moderate**

Star Sign: **Leo**

Race: **Caucasian / White**

Eye Colour: **Green**

Height: **5'9" - 6' (1.71m - 1.80m)**

Hair Colour: **Light Blonde**

Build: **Muscular**

Hair Length: **Short**

Appearance: **Attractive**

Facial Hair: **Clean Shaven**

Smoker: **None**

Drinker: **Light**

Vegetarian: **No**

Interests: **Pop Music, Movies, Theatre, Dancing, The Arts, The Outdoors, Restaurants, Pubs / Clubs, TV / Radio, Internet, Travelling, Sports (Watching)**

I'm sure he's a perfectly lovely man so I'll forgive him his punctuation and spelling errors and say no more. Except - I'm now getting a tiny bit concerned. There seem to be more men resembling someone's dad or even granddad contacting me than average to good looking guys my age? Hmmm what does that say about me?

Message From Paul:

You're sarf of the river, I'd be all over you like a rash otherwise. I think you're a honey.

I'll get me coat..................

Now this simply smacks of laziness. The distance between our locations is minimal. On the other hand the distance between his photo and what I find attractive is insurmountable. I'll just click on his profile for fun. I bet it's a cracker.

More about Paul and what he is looking for:

Our eyes meet across a crowded bar. You've not turned away to throw up! A good start as far as I'm concerned. I wander over, drink in one hand, Dutch courage in the other. I engage you in small talk hoping to break the ice. "Do you come here often" is so 20th Century. I know you're not supposed to ask a lady her age, so I'd probably just ask you how much you weigh. You'd be impressed. Especially when I order a Baileys with Tomato juice. I'd sip it down, lump by lump, staying cool. By now, my Dutch courage would have kicked in. I'd tell you the stories of me saving baby Dolphins from flaming helicopters. The stories of how I had turn down the part of James Bond because I had something important to do that weekend. Hopefully the ice would have been broken by now and you'd ask me for the truth. "THE TRUTH, THE TRUTH, YOU CAN'T HANDLE THE TRUTH" would be my reply. I taught Jack Nicholson everything

he knows. If you want the real truth, get in touch. P.S "The games up Goldfinger" he says in his best Sean Connery accent.

Just as I thought ... and yes, FYI, he was also bald. Is hair becoming a rare commodity?

Today my message inbox is empty, so I shall view "My Favourites". These are people who I've found doing searches. I have to say, some of them are actually not bad at all. I will email a few. See what happens. I will only be brief:

Message to Robert:

Hi Robert,

Loved your profile and photos.

Hope this year has been good to you so far! Would be lovely to hear more about you.

Jo

There, that should do. I've sent ten in total. I wonder when they'll reply? Perhaps it works better this way, rather than waiting for them to contact you? Having looked at "My Favourites" and compared them with "Who Likes You", there's a worrying discrepancy: "My Favourites" contains a gallery of handsome men and "Who Likes Me" is packed to the drawstring with old, bald, fat and mostly bespectacled men. This doesn't bode well.

Another Ten Sell-By Date Concerns:

11. You've now reached the stage where "less is more" in the make up department. No longer can you wear bright colours without resembling Barbara Cartland. "Naturals" and "neutrals" are what the gay guy on the make up counter helpfully suggests.

12. Semi permanent hair colour just isn't up to the job any more. Nope, it's permanent now and forever until you yield to grey.

13. Nasal hair.

14. Sex? Pah, you'd much sooner have a nice cup of tea and a slice of cake.

15. Despite exercising three times a week, cellulite is still making its merry way from the top of your thigh down to just behind your knee! This frustrates you as you see women in the gym twice and three times your weight who have perfectly smooth butts and legs.

16. Pushing every pram is a child.

17. You love "Strictly" and are not afraid to say so in public.

18. You're now paying three or four times the amount you used to on a good quality moisturiser.

19. You're considering having your teeth whitened. Not professionally you understand. Far too expensive - you are currently thinking about buying the equipment yourself from eBay.

20. You've never and will never watch or be interested in Big Brother no matter what channel it is on or who is in it.

I found this useful - thought you would too.

No Joke July

About Jo:

I'm optimistic, ambitious, caring, have a quick wit and a loud laugh. I am extremely close to my family and believe that is important. I have a good network of friends both male and female and love them all dearly. I believe you make your own luck and that the hardest working people tend to be the luckiest! My ideal partner would be sensitive, considerate, funny, ambitious and HAPPY! He'd also be tall (at least 6 foot), with a full head of hair, easy on the eye and in shape.

What's that you say? Call me crazy but I confess. I hold my hands up. I've signed up to another dating site! Just to see if they differ. *"Yeah right"*, I hear you cry. Well, I started to think - what if my Mr Right was online but on a different site? So, two sites have got to be better than one, don't you agree? Whilst completing a much longer and more tedious online form I came to the pets section below:

Pets I have [tick]:

Birds

Cats

Dogs

Exotic pets

Fish

Fleas

Gerbils / Guinea Pigs / Etc.

Horses

Reptiles

Other

There I was diligently going through the list when I reach FLEAS ... FLEAS! Does that mean that people seriously either keep fleas, would like to keep fleas but can't, or - most shockingly - have no opinion on fleas? I'd also wager that if gerbils and Guinea pigs could read they'd be outraged at being lumped together when they're quite clearly very different mammals. Rabbits, I notice don't even rate a mention on a list where fleas are higher up than gerbils/Guinea pigs, horses and reptiles.

Just been doing a search on the new site:

About me and what I'm looking for:

i would like to have so lovely and beautiful lady who is so serious woman and looking for very serious relationship who wants so serious relationships and i would like her to be so sensitive woman and know everything about sex and love and wants so serious relationship

I'm getting the distinct impression this guy isn't much fun.

Favorite Hot Spots: **i would like to take my partner to a small island in greece to be both of us there in romantic place and also i would like to take her to an italian resturant**

Favorite Things: **my favourite food is the japanese and the italian food and my favourite colour is the blue and my favourite music is the reggae and the jazz music**

My favourite food is THE Chinese.

My favourite colour is THE red.

My favourite music is THE The (an actual old band from the sixties I think)

Let's check out his opinion on fleas:

Pets I like: **Birds, Dogs, Exotic pets, Fish, Fleas, Gerbils / Guinea Pigs / Etc., Horses, Other, Reptiles, Cats**

He likes them and has put cats last. Do you think people are reading Fish, Fleas too quickly and mistaking it for Fish and Peas?

Message From Rod:

Hi Jo,

I would love to apply. You won't regret it. Take care

Rod

Rod has not attached a photo and I'm not sure he understands the whole internet dating concept. He appears to believe that he's applying for the position of my boyfriend. Shall I send an email back asking him when he's available for interview?

Message From Mike:

Hi Jo,

My name is Mike, I live in Gravesend. I liked your profile and photo and would like to know more. If you would like to know more about me,just send me amessage.

Mike

Sorry Mike but my first instincts based on your photo and message are negative. Let's see if your profile can make me change my mind?

Mike and what he is looking for:

Hello, So I've caught you're attention so far, so why not go a little further. Why would'nt you want to meet me, I have an easy going personality, i have a wicked sense of humour, friendly, love kids, animals, romantic, non smoking, like nights in/out, walks, beach, travelling, pubs, restaurants,I have a cat named puss, I work in South London. would like to meet someone who is honest, genuine, friendly

What is it with these guys and their infernal moggies? I admit I had a hamster when I was four that I named "Hammy" which is a forgivable name for a four year old to come up with. However, a forty-six year old man who can't think of a better name for his cat than PUSS! Give me a break.

Message From Andrew:

Hi Jo,

You look and sound great, and i think we'd have a few things in common. So check out my profile, and drop me a line.

Take care, Andrew

Okay Andrew, sure I'll check out your profile. I can see already from your photo that we have a lot in common. You too have a tiny moustache, which, if it wasn't for the invention of Immac/Veet I would share with you.

More about Andrew and what he is looking for:

Hiya, Andrew here. I'm sure everybody says it, but i really am just a nice, genuine sort of bloke. I'm kind, caring and sensitive, and a little shy until i get to know you. I'm fairly intelligent, and well educated.I'm well travelled, having been about a fair bit, mainly in Africa and South America. I have a good sense of humour, quite dry and maybe a little sarcastic. I'm quite domesticated (for a guy!)and i'm not a bad cook, even if i do say so myself! I enjoy cosy nights in with a dvd, lots of cuddles, restaurants, cinema, and maybe the occasional bar or club. Id like to meet someone who is warmhearted and loving, fun to be around and definitely not moody. Looks, age, size and shape aren't that important, as long as you're a good person. I've got this theory that everyone looks, but nobody ever replies to these things, so why not prove me wrong?

His last sentence gives the game away really. Enough said.

Next! Well hello! This guy looks attractive and sounds normal and amusing:

For Fun: **I'm happy to try just about anything for fun; I love sofas and I love activity. Although not golf. never golf. As to what I do do, pretty standard stuff; sports, movies, books, the indoors and the outdoors, although not in a hiking-boots way. ever.**

My Job:**work in a job I enjoy, I think that's far more important than money. not that it doesn't pay.**

My Religion: **Atheist seems a bit strong, I simply don't care about religion.**

My Education: **School in Taunton, I did biology at Exeter, graduated in '95**

Favorite Hot Spots: **I love bars and pubs, restaurants and coffee shops. I enjoy travel and particularly heat. Where would I go on a date? somewhere where we could talk, preferably with a beer or two. An ideal holiday; scuba in the maldives followed by a safari or two.**

Favorite Things: **Steak, early mornings, late lie-ins with laughter, late nights in quiet bars, movies that cost over 200 million, movies that cost less than 2, playing sports, good music, manchester, the back pages, enjoying work, writing, good comedy. kissing.**

Last Read: **The last book I loved was the life of Pi. But I also read fantasy novels (My secret shame).**

About me:

As to who I am? well, frankly, if that exhaustive and painful questionnaire hasn't fleshed it out then, short of providing x- rays and dental records, I've not got much else to show.

I think I may send him an email. Let's check his pet situation first:

Pets I have: **Gerbils / Guinea Pigs / Etc.**

Pets I like: **Birds, Dogs, Exotic pets, Fish, Horses, Other, Reptiles, Cats**

Ok so he's got gerbils AND Guinea pigs. Hmmmm. On the plus side fleas do not enter the equation. I shall email forthwith:

Hi

Fantasy novels, Gerbils AND Guinea Pigs?????

I look forward to receiving dental records, x-rays and your 25 metre swimming certificate.

Jo

Sounds fine, I think. Let's see if he really does have a sense of humour?

It would appear not as I never heard from him again. I like to think his subscription ran out. It's my way of coping.

My dad had a picture of Mohammed on
the Mount like this. OK so he didn't
have a beaker of gin in his hand but
other than that exactly the same.

Optimistic August

Been online for a while now and only one disastrous date. Perhaps in this modern society they're waiting for me to ask them? I have, however, had previous nightmares asking men out on dates. Every man I've ever instigated meeting has been less than gentlemanly in the "buying the first drink" department. Now, I'm a modern woman. I certainly never expect a man to pay for all the drinks or dinner. I'm more than happy to go Dutch. I do, however, think it entirely rude when a guy doesn't offer you a drink when you arrive. Is that wrong?

49-year-old man

London, Greater London, United Kingdom seeking women 32-42

within United Kingdom, London

Relationships: **Divorced**

Have kids: **[No Answer]**

Want kids: **Definitely**

Ethnicity: **White / Caucasian**

Body type: **About average**

Height: **5'7" (170.0cms)**

Religion: **[No Answer]**

Smoke: **No Way**

Drink: **Social drinker, maybe one or two**

About me and what I'm looking for:

I live in london.fit & slim. I am a Director of a company in the City of London. Iam good looking & have a good sense of humour. i am very loving ,financially secure ,and want someone to share my life with. I like reading, dancing, ice skating, horse riding, cycling ,walking in the countryside',driving, relaxing at home with the television and other things.I have travelled around the world quite a bit. i like children I am looking for a girl to share some of these things .i am also fond of art and antiques.I would like to meet a girl with a good sense of humour,,up to 66 inches high and of light to medium build.She should like eating out and generally enjoy life.she should also like going to the cinema & theatre.Iam also interested in eastern culture & food.

He's actually OK looking for someone nearly fifty. My main concerns are as follows …

He quite clearly got carried away with his hobbies and slipped in ice skating - a dead give away - he's 49! Strange way to phrase "I like watching TV". His version: "relaxing at home with the television and other things". He makes the TV sound like a person or a pet and I dread to contemplate what "other things" he relaxes with. Perhaps I'm being too harsh. He might also like relaxing at home with his microwave, iron or George Foreman Grill for all I know. My next and, no doubt, most obvious question is: What's with the 66 inches?

Being a modern girl I have no idea what that equates to … I've just located my tape measure and can confirm that it is in "normal speak" 5 feet 6" or one inch shorter than our TV hugging friend … His last sentence leads me to believe that he is in fact on the wrong site and should be subscribed to:

www.brideinaboxspeakinglittleornoenglishveryflexibleand66incheslong. com

Message From Bobby:

Would love to know why you used "brookstreet"?

I'm not sure if I'm your type of man and looking through your profile there's no mention of follically challenged hair type? lol.

However, I can tell your a good woman! It's in your eyes! You look genuine and sincere. So if you can see that I'm exactly that, by looking at mine! You've only got to look!

I would absolutely love to chat with you.

Your smile is something I don't see everyday! A real pleasure and I hope we can talk!

There are a lot of very attractive women on this site but few have that bit extra! Something you possess in the simplest of ways.

I'm really a good guy and I'd love to prove that to you, but you'll never know unless you get back to me. Which would be a real shame!

Bobby xx

Bobby, Bobby, Bobby. Where do I begin? I apologise if my profile specifying "with a full head of hair" isn't clear enough for you. I simply cannot forgive the awful sucking up. You can't tell I'm a "good woman". I'm sure readers will readily attest that I have my issues and am indeed not at all a "good woman". I'd also like to point out that informing a potential date that there are "a lot of attractive women on the site" isn't a good move. Even if you do follow it up by adding that few have "that bit extra" which somehow I manage to possess "in the simplest of ways". All in all, as an introductory message, I think the following:

a) Too long - please keep it short and sweet

b) READ my profile before you mail me

c) Try to keep your nose its regular shade rather than brown

d) Don't tell me how many other beauties you might/could contact

In case you, like poor Bobby Boy, are unable to sleep at night wondering why I chose "brookstreet" as my login, let me put your mind at rest. All my regular passwords/logins had been taken and I was losing the will to live so typed in an old address. Ooooohhhh wow how (yawn) interesting. The final nail in the coffin is that Bobby himself anticipates that I am not going to reply by effectively saying that it would be a real shame if I did get back to him ... Bobby's inbox does not runneth over.

Message From Seb:

Hi Jo,

I liked your profile and photo. My name is Seb and I am particularly well endowed and because this has been a problem in the past I prefer to get it out in the open as soon as possible. Check out my details and if you like what you see and large men are your thing then get in touch.

Seb

SEB! I am scarlet. What an opener ... I am speechless. I honestly don't know what to say. What *can* I say? I mean is it genuine? I actually kind of think it is. Perhaps it's a joke. I will check out the profile ...

More about Seb and what he is looking for

Hi, Right, what can i say as i hate describing myself as it can sound either arrogant or dull. im a down to earth cheeky chappie, im well travelled, enjoy sport and reading(well the sports pages) listening to music and sometimes even trying to dance to it! did you see me on Come Dancing.. I would like to meet a woman who is fun,sexy and intelligent and a little fiesty! I have decided too only chat to women with pictures. I mean, would you meet up with someone with a paperbag over there head!? I should also point out that I am extremely well endowed and this has caused me many problems with relationships in the past. Hence my turning to internet dating where I can be up front about it and no one gets any nasty or good surprises!

Oh my God. He IS being serious. I feel I'm in a catch-22 situation with regards to responding to his message. If I contact him he'll assume that I have an expansive "downstairs department" which when not in use doubles as a spare wardrobe. I've come across a rather well endowed man in the past and to be honest, although no man ever thinks you're being truthful, there is such a thing as too big. It can be uncomfortable and anything but pleasurable. I remember first clapping eyes on it and saying out loud, to my immediate embarrassment, "that ain't never gonna happen". But even he was oblivious to it being, shall we say, larger than average, which leads me to wonder - in awe and amazement - just how large somebody must be to feel the need to give their potential partners a written warning!

From: Tom

I came across your profile and really liked what I saw and read.

I have just moved back into the Bromley area after being away for a while (no not prison).

I am single with no children but I am solvent and like to think I am easy going and spontaneous.

Love to hear back from you Regards Tom

P.S Hope my 5'7 isn't a problem

Tom, frankly I'm still reeling from Seb's disclosure so probably not the best time to ask "Hope my 5'7 isn't a problem"? Or indeed mention prison.

Relationships: **Never Married**

Have kids: **None**

Want kids: **Not sure**

Ethnicity: **White / Caucasian**

Body type: **About average**

Height: **5'7" (170.2cms)**

Religion: **Spiritual but not religious**

Smoke: **No Way**

Drink: **Social drinker, maybe one or two**

Phew, it's his height! Sadly I'm unable to concentrate or comment on the rest of Tom's profile. I need a drink.

Sulky September

Bored, so thought I'd take a look at who has viewed me ...What the? It's a woman!?

About me and what I'm looking for:

Oh girlfriend what ARE you thinking of? This is the 21st century so update your expectations and say no to guys who can only talk about football, come home smelling of beer and fart in bed. Don't you know that this season's absolute 'must have' fashion accessory is a transgendered boyfriend??? Hasn't anyone told you they're fun to keep, handy for applying your make-up and don't whinge and moan when you take them shopping?? Tranny boyfriends are the new black! Plus, if you're the same dress size... BINGO! - darling, you just doubled the size of your wardrobe. Just be careful with that little Karen Millen number, OK honey? Take this fine example here for instance. He's the perfect addition to any wardrobe, although he does look best hanging off the arm of a slim and sexy smouldering stunner. But don't let that put you off as he's very adaptable and easily swayed by a beautiful smile and sparkling eyes deep enough to dive into. He comes with his own range of stylish accessories (flat, car and make-up), he's tall at 6' 1" (taller in heels) and has a 33 inch waist which does not hang over the top of his jeans. The rest of him is quite muscular, although he is in need of a bit of a tan. Dressing mainly at the weekend and maybe the occasional evening, when not looking like a girl he looks and sounds just like any other regular red-blooded male, minus the body hair. :-) But, whether he's in a silky Oasis summer dress and cream slingbacks or faded jeans and sneakers, rest assured he's kind, loving and good fun to be with. Try him for size and... oh my... sister, he is soooooooooo you!!! So... ladies... forget about those

antiquated boyfriends you've know in the past (they're like...
soooo last century) and be the first in your street to have a new
transgendered boyfriend, a boyfriend who knows just how tough
it is to drag yourself away from the Clinique counter. :- D

I am strangely drawn. Who'd have thought it? I quite like his/her
attitude and he/she certainly sells his/herself well. There are as he/she
points out many pluses to having a transgender boyfriend. I'm sorely
tempted. He/she has attached thirteen photos so I do get the
impression that he/she fancies him/herself as a model of some kind.
Also I note that he/she has out of thirteen photos decided not to
include any of him/herself as nature intended. By that I of course don't
mean nude. I mean dressed as a man. I'm intrigued to know what
he/she looks like as a man. I also admire his/her bravery, honesty and
humour. I bet we'd have a great night out. *No, stop it! You can't seriously
be considering going on a date with a transsexual?* Well, to be honest, I have
been out with weirder guys disguised cleverly as regular chaps. At least
there would never be a dull moment. I'm finding it hard to picture our
wedding album. He/she would, I guarantee, want to be a bride too and
I fear I couldn't stand the competition and pale at the thought of my
husband looking better in a wedding dress than I do. Perhaps not ... I
do however feel the urge to email him/her to find out the details about
transgender. I'm familiar with the terms "transsexual" and
"transvestite" but am not sure I know the definition of someone who
is transgender. I shall look it up ... my ancient dictionary was of no use
so used a search engine ...

"...if you really *must* have further labels to try and break that
down, transgendered people are those whose sense of self places
them so far into the opposite camp to the one suggested by their
physical sex characteristics, that they take varying steps to solve
the conflict by altering or disguising those features. Again,
simplistically, those who are happy enough to merely disguise
their features using the powerful signals sent out by gendered
clothing are dubbed *"transgendered"* and those who go to the
lengths of wishing to alter their physique to completely resemble

the sex they feel themselves to belong to are labelled by medicine as *"transsexual"*. Medicine "owns" the transsexual label because, of course, transsexual people require the assistance of surgery to achieve a physical expression of who they are inside.

Usage of the terms differs, however, and has evolved over the years in line with a growing sophistication in trans people's own awareness. The above distinctions invite the assumption that "transgendered" is in some way inferior or short of "transsexual" for instance. More recently, therefore, the term "transgender" has come to embrace both ... and Press for Change and other organisations worldwide have gone a further step and now advocate the use of the adjective "trans" to describe people who, in expressing their sense of identity, come into conflict with the contemporary gender behaviour norms of their society.

We stress however that whether you use the word "trans" or older, more prescriptive, terms like "transsexual" these are adjectives not nouns. It is no more polite to say that somebody is "a transsexual" than he is "a blind" or she is "a deaf". Please remember that trans people, transsexual people, transgender people ... or whatever description you use ... are *people* first, and the "T" adjective describes only one of the many interesting and individual characteristics which make up that person."

I had no idea it was impolite to describe a deaf or blind person as such. I would think in those cases it would be pretty helpful to those around and to themselves for people to be aware of such important issues. Why are we all becoming so touchy about what we are? Why are we terrified to be truthful to ourselves and others? If someone were to describe me as, "the white, short girl with dark hair and blue eyes and as far as I can see little or no boobs" I wouldn't take offence. It's an accurate description. I can see that you don't necessarily introduce people as straight, gay, blind, deaf, short or blonde and agree these facts do not determine who they are as in personality but it does certainly describe part of what they are. I'm all for plain speaking and in my opinion it is more offensive to rename things ambiguously when there's a precise description already available. Who empties your bins? Is it a "dustman" or an "environmental hygiene technician?"

From: DyslexicGar

Hi

Full head of hair...!!

What if I was to constantly wear a hat? Gary

Those damn baldies are persistent little fellas! I suppose they have to be. Funny that dyslexic is quite a difficult word to spell and he manages that but not his name. I'm tempted to send back a sarcastic reply:

Gary

OK as long as it's a balaclava.

Jo

Alas, it would never work out between Gary and me ...

Last Read: **Not one for books really..**

If I'm honest I read 'the Sun' great sport section and celeb gossip...must just add that I think page 3 is degrading to women and therefore I only take a quick daily glimpse...!!

I may be accused of being a snob. Something I'm tending to agree with more and more these days. I think the worst snobs are, like me, struggling "pikeys" trying in vain to raise their profile. I'm also a bookworm and strangely rarely, if ever - unless tempted by a free DVD or CD - purchase a paper.

TV: **Seinfeld...Alan Partridge,**

Films: **Usual suspects, seven, pulp fiction Music - Prince, Al Green, nina simone... Food - Bacon sarnies,**

Dog: **Ralph my chocolate**

It's not every man you meet that has a huge piece of chocolate in the shape of a Labrador. Where does he keep it?

35-year-old man

London, Greater London, United Kingdom seeking women 22-32

within United-Kingdom

About me and what I'm looking for:

In the worlds before me, primal chaos reigned. Heaven sought order. But the phoenix can fly only when its feathers are grown. The four worlds formed again and yet again, as endless aeons wheeled and passed. Time and the pure essences of Heaven, the moisture of the Earth, the powers of the sun and the moon all worked upon a certain rock, old as creation. And it became magically fertile. That first egg was named "thought". Tathagata Buddha, the Father Buddha, said "With our thoughts, we make the world". Elemental forces caused the egg to hatch. From it

came a stone monkey. The nature of me was *irrepressible!*
(Oh, OK then. I'm a lawyer based in the West End, 6 foot 3, full
head of hair and all my own teeth. Often described as "striking".
Like pubs, gigs, bit of a rocker on the quiet but with a penchant
for cheesy nights out. And I'll send you another pic if you're
interested...!)

Who am I looking for? Well, I'll take it for granted that you like
socialising, pubs, etc. - I'd worry if you didn't! But you've *got*
to be passionate about *something*. I don't really care what -
everybody's got their "thing"! Oh, and a sense of humour's a
must!

He's caught my eye. I doubt we'd get on long term but might be fun to
chat. He clearly fancies himself as his first additional photo is of Colin
Firth. He does bare a passing resemblance but you can't really do that
AND tell everybody your friends refer to you as "striking" without
leaving me convinced you're probably too in love with yourself to ever
love any one else. I'm feeling frivolous ...

Hi

*I am more Elizabeth Bennett than Bridget Jones. Which are you -
Colin Firth or Huge Grunt?*

Jo

By that I suppose I mean: own up, are you a boring accountant type or
a man who likes to receive BJ's from prostitutes in the back of taxis?
Ladies and gentlemen place your bets now.

Sadly, he too never replied. I am of course devastated. Took me at
least, oh, five to ten seconds to get over it. However, I feel it would
take a lifetime for him to get over himself.

SINGLES LOG: DATE NUMBER TWO

The Lisping Policeman

Actually he used to be a copper, but is now a TV producer. He does, however, have a lisp. We were supposed to meet at a pub in Carnaby St. I was already in town and finished at 5.30pm so I did a little window shopping and had my make up done by the loveliest chap on the Yves St Laurent counter. Really looked great and he was very knowledgeable on the product range. I have no idea how they remember the names of the hyperdermie diggery do das. So all fresh faced and feeling gorgeous I arrive ten minutes early so get myself a drink and check my messages. As I'm doing so I receive one from him.

Him: Taxi not here so might be ten mins late.

Me: *Late? On first date impressive!*

I decide that it is better for me to be honest and let him know that frankly I'm already underwhelmed. Not a great start.

Him: They tell me traffic is bad and it's a work taxi so no
            control over it. I will make it up to you.

Me: *Hmmmmmm!*

What a crock of shite. If that had been me waiting for a cab I'd have caught the train and made sure I was there on time.

Him: Are you going to be a tough one?

Me: *I could say. Are you going to be a disorganised pain in the arse?*

Nothing worthwhile is easy.

As you can probably tell at this stage I'm past caring and frankly am looking forward to catching my train home. I'm certainly not remotely bothered letting him know I don't appreciate being sat in a pub on my own and being warned that my date is going to be late ten minutes before he was due to be there. Not good enough I'm afraid.

Him: I know the taxi has really pissed me off I booked it four hours ago.

Me: *Let's call it a day if you were that bothered you would have paid for a non work cab or caught the train and been on time?*

At this point he calls me. I stress that he knew I had to kill two and a half hours as he couldn't meet until eight and being late is hardly a good start. He grovels and pleads and promises he can be on a train and with me in twenty minutes tops. I'm not convinced and tell him I'm going to make my way home. He asks me which station and says that his train goes into that one too so he'll meet me there. I reluctantly agree.

I arrive first. Surprise, surprise. He walks in and I reprimand myself for not putting my foot down and going home. His profile said he was 6"1 but in reality he is nearer 5"9 and he's obviously eaten a few pies since the photo on the site was taken. He's not obese but he's certainly not the shape he once was. He buys some drinks and settles down. He then proceeds to bore the pants off me for an hour. He talked about himself, his job, his previous job (policeman) even showed me his graduation photo from cop college. He's sandwiched between his proud mother and father (not in the pub now but in his graduation photo). My eyelids are getting heavier. I immediately find myself

78

completely and utterly mystified as to how I came to be here. I ask him why he wanted to be a policeman and he says "to make a difference". I ask him if he really believed one constable could make a difference. He says yes. I ask if the force is as racist and homophobic as they say. He denies being racist and tells me three of his current work colleagues have recently left their wives for men! THREE!!! No wonder we're all struggling. He stresses, again unprompted, that he's neither homophobic nor racist. I, out of boredom and because it's my nature to be sarcastic, respond with "so you've had sex with a man of colour then?" He looks miffed and I drain my glass.

He then talks about his ex-girlfriends, Ruby, "The Big One" - not in size but as in long term - and Camilla - the most recent - both of whom he is still very good friends with. I wish they were here now so I could leave. He then tells me he's seen Les Misérables no less than seven times. SEVEN. I'm now of course convinced he actually IS gay. I try to steer the conversation in my direction and mention he said he came from a family of actors so ask him if both his parents acted. He says "No, the only actor in my family was my alcoholic uncle who once had a small part in the Bill. Who hasn't?" Well, erm, I haven't actually Mr. We finish our drinks, I put on my coat and we leave. He walks me to the station. He says "It was lovely to meet you" and I say "Thanks for coming, eventually" and head for the train. I'm sitting on the train reading my book and I get a text:

Him: Was it Les Miserables 7 times that put you off?

Me: *No. That I could forgive.*

Him: Time keeping is my favourite pastime so don't feel it's a habit. I ran like Usain Bolt to get there for you. I am glad I did in the end. Although you may feel differently?

Bloody cheek!

Me:	*You ran because YOU were LATE it wasn't just for ME it was for your own benefit too remember.*

He's clearly got issues. Already I get the impression that nothing will ever be his fault and he'll be a total blame-meister. Why didn't I go home?

Him:	If u don't want another meeting when I am on time just say. I am a gentleman.

Freak! He is rubbish. Exactly why would I take the chance of almost being stood up again? I think he's made it perfectly clear he is NOT a gentleman.

"Aha yep," you say. "Single and going to be FOREVER". Oh I know I'm hopeless. What you don't understand is just how tough it is. It's simply unacceptably rude to inform someone ten minutes before you're due to meet them that you're still at home. It's very simple - first impressions count. Oh, and if you've been in the police force I'd keep it under your helmet and certainly wouldn't carry a photo around with you in your wallet. I wonder if he's got a cat? I can tell you're still not convinced by my "Woe is me plea" earlier - okay I'll spill:

* * * * *

Rejection and Me

I've learned to cope and expect rejection on a weekly if not daily basis simply by choosing to follow my dreams of being an actor and writer. Being rejected emotionally is a step too far for me and I don't cope with it well at all. *You don't say!* Shut up. I realise that I can often, when in relationships, feel the need to smother my partner with my need to please and feel wanted and needed. This makes perfect sense when day after day I turn up at castings where I'm usually one of at least fifty others that will also be rejected. These rejections are harder to take than most because we actors are not told. We're never told we don't get the job. Oh no we don't get:

"That was utter crap Miss Burke, we won't be calling you". Followed by "You clearly have no idea how to act and frankly although you are probably a healthy weight you read as FAT on camera ... NEXT!"

That's what I'd actually prefer to hear. Instead you get this:

"Thanks - can you tell the next person to come in".

You really have absolutely no idea how well or badly you did and you're as surprised as your agent when you actually get a job. Conversation goes as follows:

"Hi Jo"

I immediately think *oh no it's my agent. I'm being rung to be told I'm being taken off their books* and perspiration starts to gently run down my forehead.

"Jo you still there?"

"*Yep*"

"They want you for the ...job"

"*Great*" (big sigh)

"You are booked on a flight to Berlin tomorrow at 9am"

So you see we're not expected to have real jobs or lives in between castings and getting roles. Everyone involved seems under the impression that all actors come from wealthy families or have rich hubbies or wives that can finance them so all they do is go to castings. Then they can sit around at home waiting for someone to say they have the job. Immediately they can jump to action with no need to book days off work, get dogs put in kennels or children with in-laws. Nope we are at their mercy and do you know what? I ABSOLUTELY HATE that part of it.

I'm not trying to make excuses for my behaviour. *Yes you are!* What? *Oh yes you are.* All right shut up, you're right I am. It's hard, much harder than I ever let on to anyone. *I know.* I know you know but they don't. *Tell them then.* OK I will then. I was going to anyway so don't think you made me. *Yeah right.* Anyway as I was about to say I don't think anyone other than another actor can understand the sheer frustration of travelling to castings full of hope and travelling back full of ... nothing. All we're looking for is a kind word, some encouragement, perhaps the chance to do it more than once. To have a real idea of what it is the directors want. This is, of course, impossible because 99% of the time it's blatantly obvious they haven't got a clue either. To make matters worse, now I'm getting older the casting directors sometimes appear like a bunch of school kids, huddling together giggling without a clue. I bet they sit there when they know they've seen the person they're going to use and make the others do ridiculous unrelated things.

Believe me, as an actor, if a director tells you to imagine you're sitting on a potty having a wee and a child walks in. you do it. Yes I've been asked to reproduce that exact scenario and yep, you guessed, I didn't get it. I did get a call back where I had the pleasure of doing the same scene again with more people in the room. The call back could appear at first to be a good thing. But to an actor it's not. To an actor it means this ... They liked you the first time but not enough to cast you. So you need to go back and be even better and even if you are better you won't necessarily get the job - and to not get a job after being seen twice is worse.

In my case the harshness is doubled because I not only pursue acting but writing. So I regularly receive "Dear John" letters from publishers who I suspect haven't even taken the time to read what I've sent.

You may say, well, it's my choice to pursue these things and if I don't like it don't do it. Sadly though acting and writing are more than mere choices for me. I grant you they're not as commendable as becoming a NUN (even though I would technically qualify) but it's a vocation none the less for me. I honestly felt lost before I realised acting was the career for me and frankly if I couldn't write my thoughts down I'm certain I'd be madder than it could be said I already am. So really for everyone's sake it's best that I'm allowed to carry on. Quick someone, administer a pen - she's going to blow!

The first time I was on television I was naturally quite chuffed. I told all my friends what channel and time and they said they'd tune in. However, when I told my Mum she greeted the news with "Thursday at 9pm?" "Yes" I say. "I won't be able to watch that, its bingo night I'll tape it and watch it later". I felt crushed. Taping it and watching it later is just not the same. I wanted her to be as excited as I was. I mean how often is your child on national television? How many other mum's would consider this a reason to miss bingo just once? She knew she'd hurt my feelings. I'm not what you would call an expert at hiding how I feel. So I snapped, "Let's hope I don't win any Oscars on *bingo* night. My speech would go: "I would like to thank everyone involved; my hairdresser, my manicurist, my chiropodist, the Polish guys that clean my car but an extra special thanks must go to my beloved mother without whom I would not be possible. She sadly can't be with me tonight ... (dramatic pause) as this prestigious award ceremony has fallen on her bingo night". Talk about keeping your feet on ground.

Just a little tip for friends of actors ... never NEVER ask what's in the pipeline. Unless you're Keira (pan face) Knightley or Johnny (phwoarr) Depp I can safely say we NEVER have anything in the pipeline. We are as usual waiting for a phone call to tell us to be somewhere the next day. You'll hear us shouting from the hilltops when that happens. So don't enquire, it's too harrowing.

Is it really any wonder then that not being in a stable relationship adds fuel to my neurosis and feelings of insecurity? Coping with career rejection is one thing but emotional rejection on top of that is quite another. It's becoming clearer as I write that I handle neither of them as well as anyone would imagine and quite regularly make a hash of the lot. It's our secret, don't tell anyone.

Take that out. What now? *"Don't tell anyone" when you know full well it's in a book. For crying out loud do you think the type of person, if indeed there is one, that would buy this book, will appreciate your cutesie 'you're my friend now' bull? Do you?* I thought it was funny. *That might well be why you've not been published.* SHUT UP. I will get published eventually. *Oh will you?* Yes I will, even if it's purely to shut you up. *Vanity publishing doesn't count.* I SAID SHUT IT! Even I wouldn't stoop that low. Would I? Have I?

Okay

(this is getting ridiculous)

October

I've just logged on to Amazon to order a book and today they're recommending for me the following:

Is It Just Me Or Is Everything Shit?

Alan McArthur and Steve Lowe

I Can Make You Thin

Paul McKenna

Oi Pikey: A Celebration of Cheap Living

Carrie-Anne Brackstone and Laura Bushell

I'm incredulous. The above books are NOT a joke, they really do exist. If you don't believe me check them out on Amazon. Just who the hell do they think they are? Or more to the point, I am? I've ordered from them previously; *Monologues for Women, Emotional Intelligence, 100 Haiku poems.* My question is - why do these particular books lead them to believe I'm an overweight, skint pikey who thinks her life is shit?

Cheek! I'll be the judge of that "THANK YOU VERY MUCH AMA-BLOODY-ZON". Honestly. As if I don't have enough to deal with.

From: Henry

I'm Henry.

As I was browsing I saw your profile.... I have to admit... you sound interesting..

And of course you look very nice... ;-)

So ... write back to me i would like to get to know you ...

I know you must get tons of emails so I won't be surprised if you don't reply back.

(But it would be nice to know where I Stand)

I have web cam so you can see me better... and if you are nice... I might do some funny faces :-P

Anyway... I hope to hear from you soon..

Henry

p.s.

"Life is not about how many breaths you take... But how many times someone takes your breath away"

I'd be delighted to take your breath away Henry - literally. Sorry Henry. No real reflection on you. I'm I still reeling from my Amazon insults. No amount of funny faces pulled by a stranger would lift my mood. Anyway, what's with the web cam? I mean how cheap is that date? No travel fares, no purchasing of drinks and/or food. I do hope web cam dates are not the way forward.

37-year-old man

seeking women 28-35

Relationships: **Divorced**

Have kids: **None**

Want kids: **Definitely (2)**

Ethnicity: **White / Caucasian**

Body type: **About average**

Height: **2'11" (90.0cms)**

Religion: **Christian / Catholic**

Smoke: **Occasionally**

Drink: **Social drinker, maybe one or two**

About me and what I'm looking for:

I am a very caring and loyal person i have been on my own for 2 years now with a few pointless relationships under my belt . I am looking for some who is compatible with myself to spend qaulity time with, dates, holidays ect. Looks are not the most important thing to me a good personality wins me over all the time.However a 36 bus has never been apealing to me hope this dosnt make me look shallower than a tea spoon but one must have what one wants.

My aim is to meet some who i might settle down with one day but continue having fun with. I can be a practicle joker so a sense ov humour is a must.

I do hope for his sake that he's made a typo with regards to his height. He doesn't attach any photos but I'd wager he's not a looker. I'm also concerned that he feels his past relationships were "pointless" … good to know he's not bitter and twisted. Honestly we've all had our share of failed relationships but I would absolutely not think of any of them as "pointless". Hopefully even when things don't work out you learn more about what it is you're both looking for and who you are. Then you burn their clothes, pour four litres of white emulsion on their sports car and let bygones be bygones.

Let's see what else he has to say for himself …

Favorite Hot Spots: **I like to eat in theme restruants one that i go to is called Cafe Sol the waiters have mexican hats bigger than the tables. I have just spent Xmas NY in Tenerife with two mates but i am looking forward to spending my next holiday in female company.**

I've changed my mind. Who could resist a lifetime of quiet, romantic, candlelit THEME DINNERS!!!!!!!!!!!!

ARRRRGHHHHHHHHHHHHHHHHHHHHHHHHHHHHHHHHHHHH
On the bright side, he doesn't mention a cat …

Let's see who else has viewed me?

43-year-old man

seeking women 32-37

within all locations

Relationships: **Never Married**

Have kids: **Yes, and they live away from home (More than 3)**

Want kids: **Definitely (1)**

Ethnicity: **Black / African descent**

Body type: **Athletic and toned**

Height: **6'2" (188.0cms)**

Religion: **[No Answer]**

Smoke: **No Way**

Drink: **I don't drink alcohol**

About me and what I'm looking for:

This is My Love Story…

I am a confident & strong guy, shy at times, apart from when I am at the gym doing something awesome, a lot of people believe that I am very kind & caring to that degree where it could be my downfall, but that is the way things go.

I adore children and I think that they should have that spark that make's us pick them up and say: "I Love You Umm", funny, love and a lot of happiness, plus the noise to go with all this!, before they grow into one of us, and this includes the nice mummies 2. !!

I don't believe that any woman should be behind a man, but along side him, so that we can be the best ever and dance the nights through.

I don't expect anyone to Mirror- me, as we all have our good and bad values, I am not that person who sit on the edge of my seat in negative territory, but the guy who take's negativity out of the equation and crave new adventures.

I know what I want regarding finding that "Emerald" in the mist of the storm" and here are the guide lines:

Freckle face, (is nice!) you are nice to be with, and to know how to adapt & overcome, when the going gets tough in life, and to know their is extra love on the menu with a cup of "Earl Grey Lady tea", delicately flavoured.

To know that fair-play is safe-play, and tomorrow could bring to your life, additional cuddles & further laughter.

I also believe in judging people by the content's of their character, and their in-bred qualities, more so than the small print written, and their PhD's.

Plus, to remember that this journey doesn't start until you take the first steps for woman kind.

First steps for woman kind? Lady tea? LADY FECKING TEA! You just keep on being awesome in the gym. I'm sure you'll eventually attract someone with freckles (AKA ginger) I'll remain firmly sitting on the edge of my seat in negative territory. THANK YOU VERY MUCH.

Wait a God damn minute - NOOOOOOOOOOOOOOOOOOO!

OH MY GOD ... OH MY GOD. My ex-boyfriend has popped up in the "Who's Viewed Me" section. I said this could happen. I didn't dream it would. I was actually joking. This is my worst nightmare. OH ... MY ... GOD ... My dilemma now is: he obviously knows I'm on the site and he knows I know, but if I look at his profile he'll know I've viewed him. Whereas, if I don't view his profile, he may think I missed him or that I'm simply not remotely interested in how he's representing himself to potential girlfriends.

Oh shit bugger shit shit shit ... Actually he's chosen a terrible photo to use. I wouldn't fancy him from that one and I lived with him. Yes, it's the "egg freezer". Bet he doesn't mention that little gem of advice on his profile. Can I resist the temptation of seeing what he's written? Yep I can. I definitely can resist. I'm not in the least interested and will not give him the pleasure of knowing I took the time to view him. I'm in shock. I wasn't expecting that. Of all the dating sites, in all the world, my ex-boyfriend had to log on to mine ... Bugger ... I suppose the good thing about it is that he too, obviously, still hasn't found a replacement. Slim pickings out there, my friends - slim pickings indeed.

This is enough to drive you to drink …

No! Vember

I've just arrived home from having a smear. *Nobody wants to know that!* I know but I have to tell someone. *Someone okay I get the some "one", you are telling EVERYONE!* Ah so you think I will get published then? Aha gotcha! Anyway sshhh back to smears. Never a pleasant experience I think you'll agree? Somehow I seemed to have booked my appointment with the "comedy" nurse.

I arrived, de-robed and assumed the position. The nurse (I apologise in advance for this) inserts the clamp and levers me open. She then stops, looks about forlornly, starts opening various cupboards and drawers in search of something. She taps at each of her pockets. For an awful moment I think she's done one too many smears early in the morning and this is the one that's tipped her over the edge. I'm thinking, nervously, "She wants out. She's looking for her car keys and is going to make a run for it!" Eventually she casually announces she can't find any swabs. Now you might think she'd have had them to hand before clamping me open. She then says "I'll just pop upstairs and grab some, won't be a mo - stay there" and before I could say a word she was gone. "STAY THERE!" Yeah that's a good one. So there I am on my back legs akimbo with my insides getting a rare glimpse of the outside, praying that I don't hear a car engine start! After what seems like forever she returns with "Only me". *Only fecking me!* She seems amused by her remark. "Got them." She waves them about frantically. "I had to look *everywhere*" she says rolling her eyes. Is she expecting me, in my position, to say "poor you"?

If that wasn't bad enough she then goes on to moan about my tilted cervix which seemed to cause her difficulties. Then upon closer inspection (I was half expecting her to send up a flock of canaries) and some vague prodding she announces that it's no good taking cells now as I am "full" that is "full of discharge" which would mean my having to come back another time. Whilst gazing at my insides with what looks like a normal angle poise lamp she looks up at me and says "you ARE sexually active aren't you?" It's not so much a question as an accusation. I am already feeling naturally vulnerable. Adding insult to injury by making me confess "No actually I haven't ... erm ... I'm not ... for ... three ... uh erm years". That's it, I have had enough. I want the bed to collapse in half and swallow me whole. She de-clamps, gives me a "ha ha you haven't had sex for THREE years smile" and I leave. Defeated and humiliated I stop at reception to make another appointment. At moments like these I have a huge desire to be a man. Talking of men, let's see;

41-year-old man

seeking women 25-42

Relationships: **Never Married**

Have kids: **None**

Want kids: **Not sure**

Ethnicity: **White / Caucasian**

Body type: **About average**

Height: **6'0" (182.9cms)**

Religion: **Christian / Other**

Smoke: **No Way**

Drink: **Social drinker, maybe one or two**

I have just been internet "winked" at by the chap above who, although the right height, resembles Humpty Dumpty ... Let's read, I need to take my mind off my latest shock ... Oh perhaps I should first explain it's not a real wink it's a virtual wink. So it's really a cowardly and/or time saving device to save you putting together an email to a person whose look you like. The "winkee" or receiver gets a photo of the person saying "x just winked at you" and it's your choice to either wink back (where will it ever end) or email the winker, if you get my drift?

About me and what I'm looking for:

hi im a honest and very faithful loving and careing guy i have a good sence of humour i like just 2 get out ther and have lot, s of fun im just a realy nice guy 2 be with and 2 be around .i love going away abroad on hoilday 2 the sun when i can 2or 3 time, s a year i like 2 keep fit going 2 the gym 3 or 4 times a week what im looking 4 is 4 some1 2shear my life im a very giving man and im looking 4 some1 who is honest and faithful and can be loved and who can give love 2 . some1 who can have a good cuddle up on the couch when we have a night in relaxeing with a dvd and a nice drink . i would like 2 meet some1 who likes ther own space from time 2 time as i do going out with mates and thing like that so if fit what you are looking 4 in life give wink or better still give me an email what you got 2 lose xx

What has happened to the art of writing? Bit concerned about his spelling of relaxing. Is he trying to plant subliminal clues as to his real personality? I have already concluded he has a thing about the numbers 1, 2 and 4. What else does he have to say for himself?

For Fun: **like going 2 the gym going out having lots of fun and love dancing also like going away on weekends away allso like staying in night wih a dvd and cuddling up on the couch**

My Job: **no smoker**

My Ethnicity: **im well in 2 bodyilding like 2 go 2 the show's some time's looking 4 some 1 who is in 2 a bit of keep fit allso love my dancing**

Favorite Hot Spots: **i would like 2 wine and dine her**

Favorite Things: **i like eating out and having good food i like live music and i love darcing .i like going 4 long drives when i can also like going 2 pub, s and club, s i like going 4 long walk, s 2**

Last Read: **the last thing was a zoo magazne**

Wow. How on earth did he manage to get a job as a NON SMOKER? I alone know thousands of people willing to ditch their humdrum 9-5 desk jobs to fulfill the role of non-smoker. I wonder how much it pays? I do love my hot spots wined and dined though. Clearly he's unsure about the meaning of the word ethnicity. He's mistaken it for muscularity. Let's see what else he has to say …

About my life:

Hair: **Bald**

Eyes: **Green**

Best feature: **Chest**

Body art: **Visible tattoo**

Sports and exercise: **Auto racing / Motorcross, Bowling, Dancing, Martial arts, Running, Swimming, Walking / Hiking, Weights / Machines, Cycling**

Exercise habits: **Exercise 3-4 times per week**

Daily diet: **Meat and potatoes, Keep it healthy**

Interests: **Cooking, Dining out, Gardening/Landscaping, Movies/Videos, Museums and art, Music and concerts, New to the area, Nightclubs/Dancing, Performing arts, Playing sports, Shopping/Antiques,Travel/Sightseeing, Watching sports, Wine tasting, Coffee and conversation**

Education: **[No Answer]**

Occupation: **Political / Govt / Civil Service / Military Income: $50,001 to $75,000**

Languages: **English**

Politics: **Middle of the Road**

Sign: **Virgo**

My place: **Live alone**

Pets I have: **No Answer**

Pets I like: **Dogs, Exotic pets, Horses, Cats**

Its official - you can get paid, by the government apparently, in the region of $50,000 to $75,000 just for being a non-smoker. We have all been a bunch of fools - if only we'd known. Although I would prefer to get paid in pounds sterling rather than dollars but hey I won't rock the boat. As for his favourite hot spots that's a new club/restaurant on me - no idea where that one is. Catchy name though. Last read ZOO MAGAZINE. Humpty's case is firmly closed. I would prefer my boyfriend to be aware of the difference between being, say, Jewish and keen on Aerobics! Is that too much to ask? Really?

Well I have some good news finally. 1) I have a casting/audition and 2) I have a date. The casting is for a photo of dancing lawyers/barristers. I should point out I am not a trained dancer so am likely to cause myself some mischief and rip or burst out of my suit. Annoyingly this means I now have to go to my date dressed a la twinkle-toed lawyer instead of sexy smart casual.

About me and what I'm looking for:

I'm easy going and can normally be found with a smile on my face. I'm looking for that special someone to share love and life. What is salt without pepper, Laurel without Hardy and life without love ?. A little ditty entitled A GIRL'S PRAYER springs to mind : Lord before I lay me down to sleep, I pray for a man who's not a creep. One who's handsome smart and strong, One who thinks before he speaks, when promises to call he won't wait weeks. I pray that he is gainfully employed, and when I spend his cash wont' be annoyed. Pulls out my chair and opens my door, massages my back and begs to do more. Send me a man who'll make love to my mind, knows what just to say when I ask "how big's my behind ?". One who'll make love till my body's a twitchin' in the loo, the garden and kitchin'. I pray that this man will love me no end, and never attempt to get off with my best friend. And as I kneel and pray by my bed, I look at this man you sent me instead ! . What type of man am I ? - there is only one way to find out, I look forward to hearing from YOU soon. Love Jack xxx

This is a very tricky one, all I can think of is to quote a bit of Jane Austen whom used to live nearby: "It is not time or opportunity that is to determine intimacy; it is disposition alone. Seven years would be insufficient to make some people acquainted with each other, and seven days are more than enough for others".

This guy from "Who's Viewed Me" unfortunately has ears like chopper handle bars but I have to say I thought the prayer was quite relevant. Bit of a game show host finish to the prayer though, Jack. I agree entirely with Jane Austen on that point. Jack's profile has led me to consider dating the author of the prayer and/or Jane Austen. I have a naughty urge to reply:

Dear Jack

One profile is sufficient for me to know I will never want to know.

Jo

Oh no, look. I am now receiving emails from the before I was born:

From: 1971

Hello

About me and who I'd like to meet:

Me? I am a little weird (according to my dad? - Cheers dad!) What he means is that I have a vivid imagination which inturn makes me creative. It also means that I am not very predictable (variety is the spice so they say). I have a thing for gadgets (doesn't every man?) Be it functional things or just Fun toys. For example: I bought my dad a remote controlled submarine for his birthday and now I have one in my aquarium too, though there are no fish in it yet?! I like my footie (Happy Hammer) though I don't go every week as I have to have some money for other things like shopping. I do like a good outing to Bluewater every now and then.

I'm not a great reader, I'm more of apractical person. I like to spend time doing up my flat and have found that i am quite good at it. I also spend alot of my time with my best pal entertaining his kids generally having a laugh and being childish (its as good an excuse as any). I can be serious too... when the need for being serious is absolute. Generally I like to be laughing and joking. If i make one person smile everyday then i have succeeded. I'm an optimist (well i have to be being a West Ham supporter) and the cup is most certainly half full. I'm kind, considerate, generous, caring, thoughtful, definately romantic, spontaneous and unpredictable. I'd like to find a girl of the "next door variety" A girly girl who is just as comfortable wearing wooly jumper, jeans and wellies to high heels and a little black number. I'll reveal more if you ask....

As opener I would advise against the phrase "I'm a little weird" especially when your photo resembles Matt Lucas only treble his size. Yes he's also bald ... I'd also like to enquire what is impractical about reading? I can see reading would be impractical whilst say driving or swimming. He quite clearly sees me as "the girl next door". I however, as I suppose do most people, consider myself slightly higher profile. You know, more Marilyn than Doris. By that remark I don't mean I am a mentally unstable, alcoholic who is addicted to sleeping pills and eventually would like to see myself committing suicide or being murdered in the nude leaving a legacy of conspiracy theories. Was it the Michelin man who thought she was the girl next door or was it the highly paid non-smoker? I always loved Cluedo!

For Fun: **Playing, playing, playing, erm having fun, laughing and generally playing.**

My Job: **I work as a freelance civil engineer. I also can be found supervising doors some evenings :o).**

Favorite Hot Spots: **Upton Park! Its got a great roundabout and the swings are terrific! Have travelled far and wide and have done most cities and sights in the UK.**

Favorite Things: **FLove Pasta but Jacket spud smothered in HOT Chilli Con Carne has just nicked it. Like all colour. When its raining? I'm getting wet! Sainsburys! can be found in John Lewis and B and Q also. CSI Miami. Smart casual. I think i'm running out of spa**

Last Read: **A form book for the horses at a race night that i incidentally won! Picked up "Is everything sh?t or is it just me" then placed it in the library of not so good chrimbo pressies!**

Ah ha! Clearly Amazon had my recommendations mixed up with this guy's. What a coincidence. My doors will quite happily remain unsupervised thank you.

This guy just winked at me. It's all go!

About me and what I'm looking for:

I would say i am an extroverted, good-looking, blue-eyed strawberry blond. I am into many things but particularly travelling, dining out and stimulating conversation. My friends would say i am witty, easy-going and thoughtful.

I guess i am looking for someone who is also funny, and fun to be with serious at times but doesn't take life too seriously but most of all someone i can trust!!

Beware the "strawberry blonde" aka GINGER ... Let's see what he's put in his breakdown ...

About my life:

Hair: **Auburn / Red**

Eyes: **Blue**

Best feature: **Eyes**

Body art: **None**

Sports and exercise: **Basketball, Billiards / Pool, Bowling, Running, Soccer, Golf**

Exercise habits: **Exercise 1-2 times per week**

Daily diet: **Keep it healthy**

Interests: **Dining out, Movies/Videos, Museums and art, Music and concerts, Nightclubs/Dancing, Travel/Sightseeing, Watching sports, Wine tasting, Cooking**

Education: **Graduate degree**

Occupation: **Teacher / Professor**

Income: **$75,001 to $100,000**

Languages: **English**

Politics: **Liberal**

Sign: **Libra**

My place: **Live alone**

Pets I have: **[No Answer]**

Pets I like: **Birds, Dogs, Fish, Horses, Cats**

The Jury's verdict, my Lord, is: HE IS GINGER. Nice try. Perhaps Duracell should swap their "copper coloured top" for a "strawberry blonde top"? Or maybe I'll go into B&Q and ask for some "Strawberry blonde piping". What is a girl to do? If they're not bald they're ginger.

Okay, I do realise that being ginger isn't a disease and that by being gingerist, I am probably ruling out a potential soul mate. It's just, well ... I can't help it! It's not the colour, as I happen to think auburn/ginger on girls looks fab, in fact I used to die my own poo brown hair bright copper. It's just that on men. Well. Well, it just doesn't work for me. At a real push I could live with that very dark ginger which could almost pass for mahogany. Actually I think I can face any ginger provided they don't have white eyelashes. *You're making it worse.* I'll shut up about the ginger thing then.

Yet More Worrying Sell-By Date Thoughts:

21. You recently got on a bus and were totally thrown by it not taking cash.

22. You get excited at the thought of receiving a free "cool bag" for multiple purchases at Sainsbury's.

23. You no longer bite into apples - instead you cut them up, (not to be dainty or ladylike - you know why)

24. Above the knee skirts are a thing of the past and you wish you'd worn more when you could have done without looking like a middle aged girl.

25. You put off settling down because there was so much you wanted to do and now you can't remember what you wanted to do and if you've done it yet.

26. You have one or two at the most single friends and they have usually just come out of long term relationships.

27. You forget what you went upstairs for and yesterday you put the iron in the fridge.

28. You have sneezed and released a tiny bit of wee and that's without ever having kids. Frightening!

29. You spot one of your ex boyfriends and you can't get over how fat, grey and old he looks. It never dawns on you that he may be thinking the same about you.

30. You have started to worry about not paying into a pension scheme.

Dancing December

SINGLES LOG: DATE NUMBER THREE

The Hot Shoe Chef

I'm meeting a guy who sounds interesting. He's tall, looks and sounds okay, into dancing (e.g. Lindy Hop, Salsa) etc. Always fancied a go at Salsa so thought why not? He's arranged for us to meet at a Salsa bar. Immediately I see him and I get that sinking feeling. He looks distinctly geekish. Am I actively seeking them out? I'm quite sure they don't look like this in their photos. Anyway, I put on a brave face and think "well, what the hell, we can still have some fun dancing". Unfortunately his organisational skills aren't honed and the bar isn't holding any Salsa dancing tonight. Oh dear.

Never mind! We can have a quick drink and a chat, then I can go home. HOME.

He's not a great conversationalist. Every time I ask him a question his reply is monosyllabic. I ask him about his job. He's a chef, in a posh restaurant. This gets him going a bit more. I ask him if he'd consider opening his own restaurant. "No. Why would I do that when I know all the pitfalls?" I'm amazed. I would have thought that knowing all the pitfalls would be a huge help when setting up on your own. Obviously not an entrepreneur then. Again the silences continue so I ask him more about himself, where he's from originally? How long he's been in London? That type of thing. He answers, but I note he still hasn't asked me a single question. Then he speaks voluntarily! "I don't think we should sit here and talk about the past". I almost fall off my chair. *Ummmm*, I think - *correct me if I'm wrong but we're complete strangers and are meeting to find out about each other. We can hardly talk about our future together so WHAT THE HELL ELSE IS THERE?*

Our drinks are gone and I awkwardly say I should be making a move. It crosses my mind that perhaps I'm being arrogant and that he's maybe a really chatty, fun loving guy but is just as disappointed with me as I am with him. But no, he won't let me go back to my car. He insists we walk to another bar. We walk past several restaurants. I notice he has bright green shoes on and wonder how they escaped my attention earlier. He stops and asks "Are you hungry?" I'm still mesmerised by the shoes, I answer too quickly and too honestly "yes".

Before I know it we're sat at a table looking at menus. How the hell did that happen? Too late to get out of it now - if I just don't order a starter or dessert I'll only have to go through this for forty-five minutes, tops. He takes an age to order and whilst gazing at the menu he thinks now is an appropriate time to point out that they add 13.5% service charge. I can't believe he's drawing my attention to the service charge. Then he decides to be even more informative: "you don't HAVE to pay that, the 13.5% extra, if you aren't happy with the service". GREAT. Absolutely fantastic. It's Saturday evening and I'm in a restaurant with a disorganised, unambitious, green shoe wearing tight arse. Superb work Jo. I can't even get drunk as I'm driving, so I order water.

Finally - at long last - the bill comes. I perk up again, getting a whiff of freedom. As he picks up the bill, he holds it to his chest without looking at it, tuts loudly and - I swear this is the truth - says: "This is gonna sting". At this point I want to grab the candle and set fire to his nasal hair. Instead, I of course say that I was intending to pay half, which he readily agrees to, but not before calling the waiter over to confirm that the water I had was indeed mineral water as they charge £3 for it and it arrived in a jug so he never actually saw the bottle!!!!! I silently scream, and play nervously with my napkin to prevent me scooping his eyes out with a spoon. I give the poor waiter my best "He's nothing to do with me" look as we leave. He walks me unnecessarily back to my car and we say goodbye. I drive home like a mad woman berating myself all the way.

Are there ANY normal guys left? Back once more to the drawing board.

Message From Ferdinand:

Hi Jo,

Well, hello there, Thank you for reading this message. Am I what you are looking for? If not then I wish you luck on your journey. If I am, then why don't you send me an email and we can see where that takes us. You will find that I have a friendly, bubbly and caring personality. I am a people person who loves being at home just as much as going out with friends. When I am not working I am listening to music, going for dinner with friends, clubbing, watching movies , travelling etc. I am a family person , a great friend and brother (I think anyway) whom is open and trusting (has gotten me into trouble) but hey that is life, My aim this year is to visit as many places as possible for long weekends. I am looking for someone who can make me laugh and who enjoys similar things to me. I have a good sense of humour and personality. I enjoy meeting new people and experiencing new things!!

I don't like rude people, liars or gherkins! So if you are a rude, dishonest gherkin don't bother writing to me lol, but if you're not then I look forward to hearing from you! Take care.... Ferdinand

Ferdinand looks remarkably like Al Pacino in the Godfather. We do have a couple of things in common - I don't like rude people, liars or gherkins.

More about Ferdinand and what he is looking for:

Hi All, Thanks for checking out this profile. I hate this trying to explain who you are and what you looking for in a few sentences but here we go! I am a fun loving, trustworty, thoughtful and caring person.My parents are both latin.I am upfront and honest and expect other people to be the same with me.I'm a good conversationalist with an air of confidence about me, which makes me outgoing with heaps of friends all of which are coupled off but none who have nice single sisters(joke)!

I am energetic, easy going,and affectionate I can be sensitive at times as I am a romantic at heart and would love nothing better than a night in with a bottle of red wine and a bowl of pasta "al dente" but equally enjoy going to watch a musical or trying a new restuarant in town.. I like to think of myself as friendly.I also like entertaining and reading, and the company of fun people. I don't like to rush in,and would always like to get someone over time and see what develops . I'm totally honest and reliable and an all round nice guy .But hey don't they say "nice guys finish last" If you want to know more,drop me a line.

I have no issue with him being of Latin decent. What I object to is the fact that he's Brylcreemed his hair in a side parting and is sporting a pinstripe suit in his photo. I have a strong feeling he carries a violin case too.

Message From Martin:

Hi Jo,

How are you doing? Could you watch on Tv the african cup of nation final. I am from Ivory coast and I hope we will win.

More seriously i would like to know more about you.

Anyone who opens with "How are you doing?" is wrong wrong WRONG!

Message From Clinton:

Hi Jo, you have taken my breath away ! so much so that i may be
in need of "the kiss of life", you look and sound amazing , i think
i maybe that tall romantic caring guy you are lookng for -
however i must point ut that i smoke and you have indicated no
smokers - is that a real problem for you ? Clinton X

Do you know, that email has left me in dire need of some pickle to go
with all that CHEESE. The gangster look seems to be very popular at
the moment. This one looks like Reggie Kray.

More about Clinton and what he is looking for:

Hi there, im looking for a lady that loves laughter,being made to
feel special,and looking for the love and care of a romantic and
caring man . Im quite adventurous and dont take myself too
seriously - would love to meet a special lady to share everything
with. I like eating out, travelling,experiencing new things ,up for
a laugh,i also have a very romantic and genuine caring
nature,and can be spontaneous,i also like to cook (especially for
a special lady).I also have a funny bone (steady girls). If when
you meet someone you hope the earth moves "lets hold on
together " . I

know that lady is out there - could it be you .

I feel dirty! Reading Clinton's email is like being hosed down with oil.

Message From Ali:

Hi Jo,

I don't know if I am doing this right, but just have become a paid member of this league and still to learn lot more, I thought of sending you a message after seeing your profile and stunning picture. Well I still am not very convinced this dating actually works, well "Most people learn by observation, and there are the few who learn by experimentation. And then there are those who actually TOUCH the fire to see if it's really hot." Love to hear from you. One of the most difficult question is to write something about yourself, having said that, although I am no author or a writer of any novels, I am able to write a bit more than a nutshell view of who/what I am.

Having born in 1972 to an Sri Lankan Tamil Parents, did attend the local school and eventually joined the Civil Service in 1997 and further enhanced my academic advancement in finance at Winchester Military College, followed by attending Sandhurst to become an IT literate. But still cannot master IT. I am no intellectual but have great interest in world affairs/finance from Asia to Bosnian conflict. As I work for Ministry of Defence and now based at HQ Northwood I also have great interest in where our soldiers are sent and what a great job they do around the world for peace and prosperity of human existence.

I also would like to point out here that I am an expert in warm oil massaging, which I have been enjoying.

On the social side, I love to go for a sit down meals and an odd pint at the pub, I also like walking and running. I love to sit home and watch telly, wildlife is something I enjoy, and my favourite films has to be actioned with suspend with a bottle of nice wine. Love comedy too. Music is something I enjoy mostly listen to KISS FM and love R&B.

As per my appearance I am muscular average body, tall 5 feet 11 inches, black hair/eyes.

General interests have been reading my local and nation paper, love simple thing in life. I always believed life is something that needs to be achieved with simplicity; it is our thought and complicated ideals that make the life difficult.

My quote is; Love is a desire for beauty, which transcend the physical & personal culmination". - Well that's a start - sorry if its bit elongated but at least you get most of the picture.

MOST of the picture? There's more? Life is quite simply too short. Fancy enjoying "sit down meals". Well I never? Another way of putting that last quote is: I'm frankly just looking for a shag so who cares if she's a munter. Let's see who's viewed me:

About me and what I'm looking for:

Good Morning/Afternoon/Evening Ladies

My name is Drew and these are my resolutions for this year:

1 - To stop trying to please everybody else and start pleasing myself (No! Not like that.)

2 - To stop looking for "the One" (and being disappointed) and start having some fun.

3 - To enjoy myself in the company of strong-minded, independent and beautiful women.

4 - To be a Gentleman at all times (except when it's time to be an animal).

And here are yours:

5 - To view the world with joy, laughter and optimism. (I do).

6 - To neither wait for me to call, nor complain when I don't. (Have some self-respect, girl).

7 - To not attempt to control me, tell me what I should or shouldn't do or assume you know what is good for me. (You will be laughed at, ignored, or contradicted, respectively).

8 - To be a Lady at all times (except when it's time to be an animal).

Up for the challenge?

OK! Now, give me three good reasons why we should get to know each other better.

I feel inclined to reply:

Dear Drew

As requested:

1 - you

2 - total

3 - tosser

I'm beginning to see why all these guys are single. These dating sites seem to be brimming with dyslexic, scary looking, bizarre men. Do I really need to pay an extortionate amount of money each month to meet those? It would seem I do. I sincerely hoped that these sites would be full of people similar to me. Wait! Perhaps they are. NO!!!!! Maybe guys are reading my profile and thinking the same thing? I'm not dyslexic though. Honest I'm not - if you find any spelling mistakes it's purely because the words tumble out of my head too fast. I don't think I look too scary and I'm definitely not bald. Okay I admit I MAY be a little bizarre. Oh bugger ... I've just remembered having read that it's a fact that we're attracted to people who look similar to us. This is of course a real blow. This means that the reason I'm getting so many emails from obese, aged, bald men is in fact because they all think I'm in the same league. Shit.

About me and what I'm looking for:

I, I'm no brainer, just looking to have fun and good time while in London...some days per week. I'm look for a good looking girl/wife than get bored by her wedding life, to make me think mad about her, spend some time out or on travel...

This profile comes with a photo of a very attractive man in a bath who appears to be nude - although you can only see his torso and legs, both of which 10/10. Unfortunately, as you'd expect, I'm getting the impression he's... how shall I say it? ... "A foreign good time boy". Let's see what else he has to say:

For Fun: **Feeling lonely and alone in London... look for fun and different experience..french lover**

My Job: **Meeting a lot of people, but kind of boring job..**

Favorite Hot Spots: **Why not to your place?**

Favorite Things: **fun and love...**

Last Read: **have read Wild Swan a imtimate view of China some decades ago...**

Need he say more? I think, though, he must have been a child genius as he's only thirty and the last book he read was "some decades ago" which means he was reading "An Intimate View of China" at around ten years old. Clearly he was side tracked from his genius when puberty struck.

Jog on January

Another day another wink:

Relationships: **Divorced**

Have kids: **None**

Want kids: **Definitely (2)**

Ethnicity: **Latino / Hispanic**

Body type: **Athletic and toned**

Height: **5'10" (179.0cms)**

Religion: **[No Answer]**

Smoke: **Occasionally**

Drink: **Social drinker, maybe one or two**

About me and what I'm looking for:

well you can call me grasshoper if you wish cause i consider myself tall, dark and handsome.i had few dates in the past but have not come across what i call edible, i am honest, trustworthy, and very extrovert and optmistic.and of course i hope one day what meant to be for me wont go by me unoticed. may be one day my day dream will come true, i love traveling and of course its my job so only a handful of coutries i have not been to.work took me to those countries but one DAY my princess to be will find me charming enough to take her whereever she would fancy to and i can assure you i will enjoy it too. so many beautiful places out there that i have been too but i am hoping one day some honest lady i will meet to share happiness with. being of medeteranian descent, i describe myself happy going down to earth and one day happiness will turn up

IN OTHER WORDS I MEAN I AM LOOKING FOT THAT SPECIAL LADY WHO SOULD BE TREATED AS A LADY, THE LADY OF MY DREAM, THE LADY WHOOM I WOULD LIKE TO WINE AND DINE AND GIVE HER ALL THE LOVE I CAN, SO IF YOU THINK I WET YOUR APPETITE, WHY NOT CLICK SEND FOR THE DISH OF THE DAY AND YOU MAY GET

HOLLAND, HOLLAND, HOLLAND

HOPE

OUR

LOVE

LAST

AND

NE VER

DIE

SO THIS IS TONY SIGNING OUT AND I SHALL LOOK FORWARD TO THOSE GENUINE REPLIES XXOO

I expect you're thinking what I'm thinking. These gooey doe eyed cutesy emails are what I'd expect a certain type of overly sentimental and emotionally unstable woman to send. What's with the shouting towards the end? Smacks of desperation. Where have all the real men gone?

About me and what I'm looking for:

How do I describe myself...hmmmm...well, a Mushroom. Yep, thats coz I am a "funghi" - Get it ???...Fun Guy !!!

I love life, enjoy it to the full and wake up every day looking forward to enjoying what it will bring. For me, the glass is always 1/2 full.

Sure, life isnt a 24 hour party, but I believe in making the best of everything.

I have a great and diverse circle of friends and good family and enjoy what I do for a living.

I am fully self aware - so no lack of confidence or psychological disorders with this bloke !!!.

I have travelled, so that means I must have broadended my mind !, and I am receptive to expand my mind and learn even though I left school 900 years ago.

I like going to different places, experiencing different things and being of a gregarious nature, enjoy people (mixing and talking to them).

I do have my quiet, refective moments and also thrive on a good old conversation / debate over a hot cup of tea and chocloate hob nob !!!

Life is for living - and I have no intention of wasting it - its too short and valuable not to give it a damn good go !!!

I'm afraid this man is far too hilarious for me. I could never cope with the competition. He's certainly a nob but sadly not the chocolate hob variety.

About me and what I'm looking for:

I am 51 just turned white, 5'10" separated blue eyes normal man living in SE Lon .I am 14st and losing it, I have lost 11lbs in 2 months and very pleased with myself.I do not smoke, but I like a drink and a laugh

I am solvent and like planning lots of things in my spare time from a walk on the coast or by a river to an exotic holiday in a new country.I have already travelled a lot to all continents although only briefly in South America.It doesnt have to be overseas or a lengthy trip in fact some of my faves are a weekend in the Algarve in winter just to raise the temperature or a weekend in Devon or the Lakes under canvas but only in the Summer !

I also like watching football, cricket, and occasionally horse racing and rugby and have watched all of these on trips overseas at one point or another, this has take me to less glamerous places sush as Pakistan Bangladesh Macedonia and Azerbiajan

I also like to play sports like tennis, badmington and pool with a partner for fun

I enjoy pop concerts at inside arenas but not so much the big festivals but would still go

I work varied and sometimes irregular hours but am rewarded with time off when I request it.

I like to dine out and in and know I can provide interesting and varied conversation or cook a good spicy meal if asked

I have no children but that is not because I do not like them and still haven't ruled out the option

All I ask of you is that you share some of my interests or even if you don't at least respect them I will make an effort to try to accept and understand yours and even give them a try

I want to make a friend first but need you to be honest
trustworthy and reliable and I know I can promise the same
along with loyalty and commitment

I feel I am reasonably articulate but please forgive me if I can not
provide poetry and corny one liners as I am new to this.

If you think you like the sound of me get in touch, I am far from
boring I assure you.Happy to send pic if you like sound of me

Well I certainly appreciate the respite from corny one-liners. However
I'm a tad concerned that he hasn't attached a photo. Not because he
admits to being overweight but because I'm fearful of someone with
five foot ten "separated blue eyes"! I'm also sincerely concerned that in
his first line he announced he's just turned white! What does this
mean? Has he just seen a ghost? Or has he literally just finished
undergoing Michael Jackson-esque skin bleaching? Other than that he
sounds like a decent chap.

About me and what I'm looking for:

...divorced company director, wife of 20 years ran off with best
friend...never mind, I kept everything, including two wonderful
kids..and two cats...Church warden, cub leader, sing in a choir,
love any music including, Yes, REM, Simon and Garfunkel,
Deep Purple, Dido, Norah Jones, Classical Choral (BUT NOT
OPERA!) jazz etc. etc., love Greek Islands, but off to Gran
Canaria for a week to see in the New Year. Enjoy tennis (did
until my 15 year old son started beating me) and football
(watching Palace lose week after week), cooking good food
(Crispy roast potatos, cooked while doing the ironing and
drinking Gin and Tonic...), love driving fast through big
puddles...standing on the back of a shopping trolley and
whizzing down the aisles (much to embarrasment of 18 year old
daughter..who is now at Uni)wicked sense of humour, totally in
contradiction of much that goes above - but - I'm just a normal

bloke with a lot to give to the right person - can't have more kids unless you know a surgeon with a REALLY steady hand... used to work for a multi national, but walked out on a point of principle, and started own company with some good friends...(and a lot of faith!) It is exciting and fun...! Enjoy good meals out but love nights in with a bottle of red...missing the feminine touch...(A girl friend once told me I was very in touch with my feminine side...I would rather be in touch with your feminine side...!!!;)..chilled out, laughing, sexy, happy with life and excited about the future...preferably within 20 miles of Croydon (where I am!) ...somebody who would love to regularly be given a surprise bunch of freesias...(sorry, can't afford a regular supply of diamond rings yet...!)likes being romanced... If you're looking for a sugar daddy - forget it...all my money went into my business..all I can offer is a lot of love, laughter and support for you...- beginning to notice on these profiles that women who say they are a certain age, but look much younger - generally don't! (sorry girls) I'm not keen on lots of make up or lipstick, or big ear rings (on women, not on me!) - don't mind if you are a mum - just don't want to go out with someone who looks like MY mum!, have been out for coffee with some really nice girls from this site - just not THE nice girl!

Sorry - but no photo = no reply!! Got good reasons for this! (been asked a few times...straight answer is that a description of slim in a profile doesnt equate to 14 stone in real life...also a picture that is some 15 years out of date is wrong as well!)

For Fun: play tennis.drink red wine..play ten pin bowling..drink red wine..sing in a choir..drink red wine...excellent cook...(often using red wine...)

My Job: managing Director and 25% owner of a little company...

My Religion fee paying Anglican...

Favorite Hot Spots: **Greek Islands in Summer...Canaries in winter...want to see the Great Lakes, Pompeii, New Zealand...and lots of other places as well...**

Favorite Things: **driving to Brighton on a wet Friday evening and having fish and chips on the pier...**

Last Read: **daughters copy of '19' magazine...for the pictures...!**

This man is 47 and obviously thinks swinging like an inflated bottomed monkey from supermarket trolleys and regularly perving his way through his daughter's magazines are babe magnet qualities. No wonder his, probably rather nice, wife opted for his best mate. I wish her all the best.

Message From Baz:

Hi Jo,

I saw your profile and I wish to know more about you.

Am I have chance to keep in touch with you?

By the way,I am an asylum seeker who has been in England for nearly 6 years.

Is that problem for you?

Regards Baz

Is his name really Baz? Think not do I Yoda is it.

About Baz:

Family Status: **Single**

Sexuality: **Straight**

Children: **Zero**

Education: **Secondary / High School**

Profession: **Other**

Religion: **None**

Employment: **Unemployed**

Practising (religion): **Non Practising**

Income: **Low**

Star Sign: **Cancer**

Race: **Middle Eastern**

Eye Colour: **Brown**

Height: **5'9" - 6' (1.71m - 1.80m)**

Hair Colour: **Black**

Build: **Slim**

Hair Length: **Short**

Appearance: **Average**

Facial Hair: **Clean Shaven**

Smoker: **None**

Drinker: **Moderate**

Vegetarian: **No**

Interests: **Computers**

More about Baz and what he is looking for:

180 cm height.72 kg weight in Persia. (my country) friends used to tell me:You have got key of hearts!!! Always smile.Very kind.Honest.Clean and tidy(not lazy).like talk,walk,sport and so many nice things.I love healthy life.I have got so many things to say but not now.So cheerful.Sometimes good listener.I am looking for someone who makes me happy not makes me cry.And at the end I am so peaceful.

Is Persia lacking in gravity? Does that mean he's lighter & taller here? Or does it have a greater gravitational pull and therefore he's heavier & shorter? I'm confused. I couldn't go out with someone who is only a "good listener (sometimes)". Oh well - I suppose we'll all be peaceful in the end. This is increasingly making me look forward to my peaceful end. I wasn't an asylum seeker but I am now.

Message From Trent:

Hi Jo,i,m Trent wow your a very pretty lady ,god that sounds so corney sorry about that but had to be said . hopefully your take a look at my profile and lets see . Trent x

He may well be six foot with hair but his spelling and grammar are shot to pieces. I refuse to apologise for wanting a potential boyfriend to be able to write. I'm a fair woman and, of course, if English isn't your first language I have a certain amount of tolerance. Trent attaches two photos that are identical. Either that or he is in fact a twin and they're sharing their subscription fee.

Message From Adam:

Hi Jo,

iam very happy if you see me

Weird as he hasn't attached a photo so would appear he is very unhappy for anyone to see him.

About Adam:

Family Status: **Single**

Sexuality: **Straight**

Children: **Zero**

Education: **Secondary / High School**

Profession: **Other**

Religion: **None**

Employment: **Employed**

Practising (religion): **Non Practising**

Income: **Moderate**

Star Sign: **Capricorn**

Race: **Middle Eastern**

Eye Colour: **Brown**

Height: **5'9" - 6' (1.71m - 1.80m)**

Hair Colour: **Black**

Build: **Average / Medium**

Hair Length: **Short**

Appearance: **Attractive**

Facial Hair: **Clean Shaven**

Smoker: **Heavy**

Drinker: **Light**

Vegetarian: **No**

Interests: **Reading**

More about Adam and what he is looking for:

iam agood man and iam ahard man and hard warker and ilive along and ilook for sumwan to lokafter me and ilook after her

I should perhaps check my profile hasn't been tampered with. Perhaps someone has changed it to: Jo seeks Middle Eastern (asylum seekers pref.) heavy smoker who is good, hard and wants English lessons.

For some reason pictures of Borat keep popping into my head ...

Message From Liam:

Noticed you while i was browsing on this site so i thought i'd say a quick hello to you. You seem to be a pleasant and easy going girl and i also find you very attractive. I would describe myself as an open and honest person who likes to be affectionate, though i must admit i can be a little impatient in certain situations. I have a full head of hair and often told that i have gorgious eyes but as i am open and honest i have to admit that i am only 5ft 8. I had to

look up that interesting word you used 'procrastinator' Not come across it ever. Well, i do believe that life is too short and if there is something you really want to do, buy or somewhere you want to go then just go for it. I hope you don't procrastinate on me. IF you can put up with me being only 5:8 then feel free to drop me a line. Take care. Liam. X

Probably not best to write to someone who expressly pointed out her desire to meet a tall man when you are in fact the opposite. He does attach a photo but it would be far wiser for him not to. Why do all these people presume that I'm pleasant or easy going? I think by now you've realised I'm neither of those things. His hair is frankly hanging on for dear life and probably by the time we'd organised a date would have slipped down to his neck and back. As far as honesty is concerned, although it's a trait I admire, I do think admitting to someone you're trying to attract that you have no idea what a word means is rather foolish. We all read or hear words we don't immediately know the meaning of and, if we're inclined, can look them up for our own benefit but we don't advertise it.

Time to do another little search methinks. Found a nice looking chap, right age, height AND one of his photos is of him riding a horse so we have something in common. I'll drop him a line ...

Message Sent To Hugh:

Hi Hugh,

I used to own a horse but I had to give him up when I decided to study acting then work part time. Just too expensive damn it!

How are you finding internet dating?

Jo

I hope he replies. I have to admit not one of the guys I liked and initiated contact with has emailed me back. Why is that? It would suggest I'm punching above my weight if all the emails I get are anything to go by. PLEASE don't make me settle for a balding dwarf. I simply won't. I can't do it. NOPE. I'd rather be single. Although if that were really true, and this site is anything to go by, this could mean I will die a ... I can't say it ... it's such an awful word ... *I'll say it for you gladly.* *SPINSTER!* Thanks.

I Just Can't Stop Thinking of Sell-By Date points now!

31. You can no longer get a thirty-year mortgage.

32. You no longer feel stable wearing heels.

33. You've been on the Pill so long you wonder if you are in fact biologically sound.

34. You've fallen asleep whilst out in company and not just at the cinema or theatre - you've actually nodded off in a club!

35. You've been on unsuccessful dates with all of your friends' friends and all the single blokes at work (and maybe some of the married ones).

36. You have an Anne Summers store card.

37. You could happily walk over hot coals, broken glass or even sand down the woodwork with your feet. A camel would be proud.

38. You know who your local MP is.

39. Hairy toes!

40. You look forward to receiving and reading the local paper.

More messages:

Message From Alistair:

Hi Jo,

how are you? hope you have had a good day.

i see that the theatre is one of your interests too. have you been to see any good shows recently? I hope to go and see We Will Rock You soon, have you seen it???

Nice to read that you are a loving and caring person. I like to think that i am too as i look after my mum. Hope that doesn't put you off??

take care Alistair

Alistair, can I make the smallest suggestion? Can I? Really best to avoid telling people in your first email that you look after your mum. I mean it's great that you do. I'm pleased for your mum and yes that makes you a kind, caring person who is no doubt a far better human than me. Or does it? Plenty of "carers" have been prosecuted for harming their patients/loved ones. I mean take Stephen Hawking. You can imagine his wife tormenting the poor sod. Giving him a swift jab in the ribs and waving his "speak and spell" in his face typing the word "ouch" for him and laughing manically. So I think we should all be a little bit less emotional and stop taking it for granted that a carer has caring traits. One does presume that doctors would have caring qualities, wishing only to cure and heal people - need I draw to your attention Drs Shipman and Crippen? So I suppose Alistair, dear boy, I really don't understand what you're trying to achieve by pointing this out to potential mates. Do you actually want to attract someone who feels sorry for you or pities you? Do you? Is that what you want? Or is it really self sabotage? Do you really care or are you just in it for the government funded car and benefits? Hmmmm food for thought methinks sir.

Lawks a lordy what do we have here? Is my whole world on these sites? I've just been doing a search and who should I find now? Nope, not another ex but my boss! Well actually he's not my boss any more. He left but he was. What a ridiculously small single world this is. Which would explain why I can't find a frigging new boyfriend if both sites are packed to the drawstring with people I've already been out with or already know. God damn it. I wonder how he's getting on? I could email him but maybe he'd be embarrassed. Perhaps he's not noticed me on there, I'm sure he's thinking the same. Strange. Very strange.

F**k Off February

It's officially THE most hideous day for people of the singular variety. Yep it's V-Day. I don't know why bartenders haven't invented a new cocktail. It could be called something like "The Suicidal Loner" or "The Difficult Cow" or "The Arrogant Tosser". The Suicidal Loner would need to be red in colour. Particularly potent, it should have fruit on the side of the glass and come with a free razor blade. The Difficult Cow would be black and white and be served with a perforated straw. The Arrogant Tosser wouldn't be served in a traditional glass but instead thrown straight from the cocktail shaker at the purchaser.

However, I can announce that I received an e-card today. Yippee. Somebody loves me! Ummmmm, perhaps not quite what I'd expected. It was spam and it was from Jane! I'm beginning to think they're in cahoots with Amazon. It's got to be a conspiracy. This is their latest selection of recommendations:

David Cassidy (Wall Calendar) - How old do they think I am?

Destructive Emotions (book) - What?

Counselling for Toads (book) by Claire Raynor no less?

And, wait for it, two magazines that they consider to be right up my street:

GOOD HOUSEKEEPING and ESQUIRE

I can now only assume they think I'm a fifty-year old housewife, who is not only bi-sexual but violent and therefore in need of counseling. I officially give up. Even I don't know who I am anymore. Saying that, perhaps the magazine tips are a hint: I am a messy sod. All this dating malarkey is seriously making me consider other avenues.

NB: Not a single card, flower or man in sight. Luckily I feel ill and have a pounding headache so I can convince myself that even if I did have a hot date I wouldn't feel like going. *Yeah right!* Do you know what? I blame Helen Fielding, Jane Austen and the worst culprit Barbara-frigging-Cartland for this mess. Our heads are toyed with and messed up by books, films and magazines insinuating that there are indeed living breathing ROMANTIC men out there. When I fear the reality is that they're just about as real as Unicorns and Elton John's hair. Okay there ARE single men out there - these dating sites prove that - but ... and it's a BIG BUT ... they're all a bit, how shall I put it? ... dysfunctional. *Ditto!* I shall ignore that remark. Is my happily married friend right? She said "Jo all the cups have gone. Only the mugs are left now". Wait. What's this? I have a message from the horsey guy...a potential cup surely?

Message From Hugh:

Hi Jo,

Thanks for the message. Sorry to hear that you gave up horse riding, i can fully understand why, as i'm the owner of 2. I really must be a bit mad, but there you go.

I've only been on the site for less than a week, and to be honest it's all a bit daunting. There is a lot to be said chatting to someone face to face. But i guess the problem is meeting someone who you would like to chat too. And i've also got the added complication that i can't type for toffee, so please bear with me

So how did you get into acting? How long have you been doing it? I have to hand it to you, to get up on a stage in front of people. That's a brave thing your doing.

Hope to hear from you soon.

P.s. Sorry again for the typing. Hope your having a good week.

Ah I like him more and more. He, of all people, doesn't need to apologise for his typing. Overall I am impressed.

Message Sent To Hugh:

Hi Hugh,

I know it's a strange way of meeting people but would agree that it's not meeting people in general we have a problem with it's meeting people who are also looking for a relationship.

Two horses? Blimey you've got your hands full. I used to keep mine on full livery in Wilmington, as I work in Bexleyheath so it was handy.

Believe me your typing is pure excellence compared to most. Just noticed you are based in Bexleyheath too!

Acting is a long story...tbc

Jo

Could I have stumbled across a cup and not another mug? A Cup, a cup - my very first cup! Zippidy dooooodah day!

Strangely quiet on the email front considering what day it is. I would have thought it would have been a good time to contact people. Wish them a happy Valentine's Day, ask them out for a date. But no. Very little email traffic. So, am I to believe that I'm the only single person who is actually at home on their laptop on this prestigious night of nights? Or is everyone else sitting at home trying to play it cool and not logging on to give the impression they're out having a whale of a time? Well, I've had a Weight Watcher's shepherd's pie and two bowls of

Crunchy Nut Cornflakes. Its 8.30pm so a cup of tea is in order whilst I settle down to watch "Shameless". *There's irony for you.*

I've been winked at by what looks like a pensioner:

41-year-old man

seeking women 30-46

Relationships: **Divorced**

Have kids: **None**

Want kids: **Not sure**

Ethnicity: **White / Caucasian**

Body type: **About average**

Height: **5'10" (177.8cms)**

Religion: **Christian / Catholic**

Smoke: **No Way**

Drink: **Social drinker, maybe one or two**

About me and what I'm looking for:

Hi im a hard working hard playing person i think im carring and honest. Ive come to apoint in my life where i want to be with a person i can trust and care for and she in return.I have been lucy and traveled a lot and would love having a partner.

Wow, he looks much older than forty-one. He must have had a tough paper round. Not honestly sure I want to engage in email conversation with someone who looks like an OAP and calls himself LUCY. I bet he has travelled a lot. The length and breadth of his Freedom Pass ... there's more:

For Fun: **I love to travel its only money that stops me being on the road full time.Im getting a bitt old for it now but i love playing and watching football. dont worry i donnt bore peaple with it. also love skying.**

My Job: **I run my own small building firm. mainly doing kitchens and bathrooms my religion not practicing**

You may not bore "peaple" with football but I suspect you'll devise other ways. I believe "Skying" is lovely this time of year. I'm off to not practice a religion. Now let me see which one shall I not practice today? Today I think I won't be Jewish. Tomorrow I will refuse to be Catholic.

✳ ✳ ✳ ✳ ✳

Well it's the day after Valentine's and I haven't received a single wink or email from either of the sites. I can therefore only assume that all the subscribers on both sites, in a fit of mass depression, have committed suicide. Leaving me as the "lone surfer". Is there anybody out there?

Yippeeee. Hugh has emailed back:

Message From Hugh:

Hi Jo,

Wow !!! me good at typing!!!! little do you realise that i'm in danger from getting repetitive stress syndrom, from hitting the delete key so much...... but thanks for the compliment anyway. My two horse's are called "Chunky" he's 10 and we do a bit of showjumping together,and " Ric" he's only 4, and i'm schooling him(under strict supervision". The horse in the photo is called" Angelito" who i used to ride when i was competing in France.(No i'm not that good, it was where i was living and working for the time. And how i got into horse's in the first place). Thankfully both of my horses are kept in a small private yard, at the back of Swanley Village. Owned by a friend who does me a cheap deal in livery, and in return i help him around the yard on my days off. In the eyes of some people, I to am a part timer, the luxoury of a four day on, four day off shift pattern. Also whilst in France i had a Labradour (really am a country boy at hart) who at times i really miss. I see in your profile you've a dog. What breed is it? And i must confess that the Acting story has got me intrigued. I hope i hear more about it soon.

Anyway hope your well and trying to keep dry, hope to hear from you soon.

Hugh

Hugh, don't get carried away. There's a definite deterioration in your spelling/punctuation. Still, I'll overlook that on this occasion. I actually like the sound of you. We share a love of horses and dogs (don't forget he's not bald and he's between 6"1 and 6"4). Looking at his profile again he could actually be accused of being, dare I say it, Strawberry blonde! Knickers! He describes it as light brown so I'm hoping it's the angle of the sun. I wonder if he'll suggest meeting so I can see what he really looks like.

Message Sent To Hugh:

Hi Hugh,

I have a Staffordshire Bull Terrier (Murphy), who before me had four homes and was wanted by none of them. I can't understand why he is the gayest dog in the village! Lovely nature and hates being on his own.

Sounds good - week on week off - what do you do?

I miss riding but haven't been near a horse for years now and know how much I will ache afterwards. Where do you ride - Joyden's Wood? Or do you box them up and take them elsewhere? I was never that good at it but adore animals and my horse (Arthur) was like a big old armchair to ride. So comfy and safe - a proper gent. I prefer a good-natured plodder to one that tanks off with you!

Jo

Reading that last sentence again made me realise I think that's also how I prefer my men. I wonder what he does for a living? Week on, week off? Surely he can't be a fireman? Life's just not that good ... Already my imagination is running away with me. I can see us galloping blissfully over the hills, tying up the horses, having a picnic, lazing in the sun, kissing and laughing. He'll take my hand and look seriously at me, brush my hair gently from my face and propose. I say yes, we kiss, cry with joy and gallop happily ever after into the sunset. *STOP IT!* What? *That.* What? *You always do that. Get all unnecessary with no provocation. All he's done is reply politely to your email. Make a sentence from the following: GRIP A GET. Who do you think you are? All the Bronte sisters rolled into one?*

SINGLES LOG: DATE NUMBER FOUR

The Essex Boy

He doesn't live in London, he's "based" in Essex although stresses he's not originally from there (who wouldn't stress that?). He leaves me to decide where to meet. Frankly, I'm already not impressed as I'd rather he took the bull by the horns but fair enough. I find somewhere in between our two locations: a Holiday Inn, so easy to park and near the motorway. I email the details and very thoughtfully include a map as well as time and date. A day goes by no reply, two days go by no reply, third and final day is the day the date was planned. Now, he has my email and hasn't responded and he has my mobile number and he's not called or sent me a text. So I presume that he's blown me out and I make my way straight home from work.

At 6.30pm - half an hour after we were supposed to be meeting - he calls me. Basically he's sitting in the hotel bar wondering where I am. He even has the cheek to sound aggrieved. I explain that, as he hadn't acknowledged my email or called to confirm, I'd presumed he'd met someone and was madly in love and all thoughts of our date had flown clear out of his head. He assures me this is not the case and that he would NEVER be so rude as to not show up. I feel I have to point out to him that he'd been rude enough not to acknowledge my email. He apologises and asks if I'll still come and meet him. Now, you'd think I'd learn from previous mistakes, say no and go to bed. But oh no! I feel bad he's sitting there so I get in my car and meet him.

He's okay looking but (once again) is definitely not six feet tall. WHY oh WHY do they lie? He's got a drink and food and doesn't offer to get me one so I mutter to myself all the way as I go to the bar and order a small white wine. He turns out to be a crashing bore and just as I'm thinking up ways to excuse myself the fire alarm goes. Perfect. I can make a dash for it. So there I find myself at a Holiday Inn car park in the freezing cold with a glass of wine I purchased myself with someone who didn't reply to my email and who isn't as tall as he said and I can't help thinking: *what exactly did I do to deserve this?* My teeth are chattering and I say I think it's best we go our own ways. He pleads with me not to go and suggests we sit in his car. Yeah, that old chestnut. I don't think so. Just as the fire engine arrives, decked out with six rather dashing firemen I might add, the alarm stops. DAMN IT! He looks relieved and I feel defeated. In we go again, to catch up with where we left off, which was, as I recall, with me seriously considering chewing my own arms off.

This whole process is putting years on me.
Thanks app, I now look like E.T.

March-ing On

43-year-old man

seeking women 33-49

Relationships: **Never Married**

Have kids: **None**

Want kids: **Someday (1)**

Ethnicity: **White / Caucasian**

Body type: **About average**

Height: **5'7" (170.2cms)**

Religion: **Spiritual but not religious**

Smoke: **No Way**

Drink: **Social drinker, maybe one or two**

About me and what I'm looking for:

Don't have a "type" that I go for, so unless you have 3 heads or a serious mental issue, please get in touch.

I like to think I am easy going and very intutative. My friends have described me as very kind, loyal and honest with a sense of humourI am well read and I like a glass of wine at the end of the day.

I guess you might see me reading the Guardian in a Costa coffee shop. As I said I don't have a "type" that I go for. Though if you can make each other laugh, that is all good start.

Looking for a woman to share such things as the above. It is easy to say what you would like but in the end if you feel relaxed and comfortable with each other. Am I talking about chemistry? Oh, I am not scared of commitment.

Do you suppose mental people are aware they're mental? I should point out though he's the first guy to admit to not being afraid of commitment.

For Fun: I love going to London, a walk along the South Bank on a summer evenings ending with a glass of wine at the Tate modern is my idea of a great time. But also like curling up with a good DVD on a cold winters evening with a woman.

My Job: I am a social worker with a local authority, supporting Adults who live in the community. It is a very complex job at times but it also brings its own rewards. Mainly at payday

Favorite Hot Spots: Love doing the European city break thing, going to places such as Rome, Paris and Barcelona. Been to America a few times also

Favorite Things: Can't say I have a type of book I read but so long as it is an enjoyable and thought prevoking read. Prefer white wine to red but can drink that to with food. Like comedy such as Blackadder, Eddie Izzard

Last Read: Boy in the stripe pyjamas. I go through stages with books. I will read 2 or 3 in a few weeks and then not read for 3 or 4 months.

Where else do adults live if not in the community? Is there a secret place I know nothing of? Surely there would be no one more suited to having a mental girlfriend.

36-year-old man

seeking women 25-37

Relationships: **Never Married**

Have kids: **None**

Want kids: **Definitely (1)**

Ethnicity: **White / Caucasian**

Body type: **Athletic and toned**

Height: **6'2" (189.0cms)**

Religion: **Spiritual but not religious**

Smoke: **Occasionally**

Drink: **Social drinker, maybe one or two**

About me and what I'm looking for:

hi would love to meet non superfical people... chilled hardworking guy, i just like to live life to the full work hard.been single for about a 2 years and maybe a half, lost count lol, a little bit tierd of being on my own, would love to meet if its possable my soulmate... if luck was to shine my way ...well you have to give it a try...would allso be nice to meet new people on a friendly bases ... it sounds a bit sad ...but most if not all me mates have settled down or married or live in other countrys..

just what to meet someone nice. and enjoy life to the fall.im not into playing mindgames.

Not even a wisp of hair and I'm truly amazed at the amount of grown men that can't spell or communicate using the written word. It's quite shocking. I wonder if it's a gender thing or if men are receiving illiterate emails too? It's worrying.

More about Paul and what he is looking for:

Hhmmmmmmmmm. . . . what goes in this bit then? All new to me. Suppose i can be described as an easy going fun fella with handsome looks rather than the mandatory pretty boy band charm or chisled jaw line. I love socialising, going to new places, meeting new people, making new friends, Skiing/snowboarding, summer sun and the odd spin or two on the motorbike. I like to be treated as I treat people (which is nicely because lifes to short for arrogance) I like manners, politeness, smiles, happy, kissing and cuddling (do I need my medication now?). Hates: doing this on a computer, mood swings and argueing. I'm looking for an outgoing girl who's as happy to spend a night in while her bloke cooks her a meal and plies her with wine whilst curled up watching a movie or listening to music, (must have cast iron stomach) as she is to go out on the motorbike to find a new place to visit or a new restaurant to enjoy. You tell me what you want and i'll try to help.

How's that sound?

Why do people insist on making the point that this is NEW to them? Now this guy refers to himself as "handsome" then follows that with "life's too short for arrogance" Hmmmmmmm. It's a pity he looks like the bizarre love child of Bugs Bunny and Elmer Fudd.

I'd like to say "That's all, Folks!" but no - onwards I must go…

More about Neil and what he is looking for:

ah, well I'm looking for the "love of my life", having passed valentine's day without any cards, so I thought would do something positive about it. Ideally will be someone also not previously married (though not for want of offers), up for a drink or three, who'll love my cooking, not mind me watching football (hey, it's a world cup year), and who can go along with whatever excuse we make up as to how we really met, as this still seems a bit embarrassing. oh well, here goes.....

Join the Valentine's Day club Neil, although I suppose it shouldn't really come as a surprise to either of us that we didn't receive any cards as it's quite clear we're struggling in the "significant other" department. Warning bells alert, alert. If you find it so embarrassing that you need to lie about how you meet people I suggest you don't do it. I have no intention of lying about it and, although admittedly some people may be judgmental about this type of introduction, I certainly am not ashamed. Advertising the fact that you're a potential liar isn't a good start. He looks a bit on the shifty side, similar to a stage magician or hypnotist.

From: Depak

can we chat if you please?

love Dep

Erm not really sure about that. Let's see what else you have to say, if you please.

42-year-old man

seeking women 31-35

Relationships: **Never Married**

Have kids: **None**

Want kids: **Not sure**

Ethnicity: **Asian**

Body type: **About average**

Height: **5'6" (168.0cms)**

Religion: **Spiritual but not religious**

Smoke: **No Way**

Drink: **Social drinker, maybe one or two**

About me and what I'm looking for:

I am a deeply reflective person with interest in the arts and the spiritual. I have been undergoing 18 years of higher education in the fields of culture studies, religious studies and now in psychotherapy. I wish to explore a spiritual approach to psychotherapy. well my dream is to initaite a sacred space like a centre where people could come in and play with the arts and explore the spiritual in themselves. So I am looking for an equal partner who is interested in similar journeys. This similarity could be internal as well ;that is one could be creative and spiritual in 100 ways and i am able to celebrate that in her. sacred sexuality is something i wish to learn about as well.

Sadly, I can't confirm whether or not he has hair as he hasn't attached a photo but I think I can safely say that I'm not attracted to pygmy hippies. "Sacred sexuality?" What a crock of shite! There's more ...

For Fun: **I enjoy watching movies with a lots of romance and plenty of feelings. I love to watch period films that connect with history and culture. water is my relaxing source. so swimming or walking by the river or sea are my most relaxing moments.**

Favorite Hot Spots: **TO the italian country side as well as to southern france in to small little villages with cozy coffee shops.**

Favorite Things: **My favorite food is curry especially home made ones. I love to watch movies that are deeply philosophical with a human story as well. Ofcourse i love body theatre and the experimental ones with a critique on contemporary existence.**

Last Read: **Reading about cinema and the cultural psyche. I also like to read Paulo coelho.**

Do you know I'd have preferred that he use the term costume drama as the mind boggles as to exactly what he means by "period films".

32-year-old man

seeking women 22-40

Relationships: **Never Married**

Have kids: **None**

Want kids: **Definitely (1)**

Ethnicity: **White / Caucasian**

Body type: [No Answer]

Height: 6'2" (188.0cms)

Religion: Christian / Catholic

Smoke: Occasionally

Drink: Social drinker, maybe one or two

About me and what I'm looking for:

Hi there ... Im 35 ... single ... gorgeous ... intelligent and got bees knees ... I live all by my lonesome with my cat Evie on a hill ... just south of Leeds City Centre around Junction 27 (M62) ... I enjoy pubs and clubbing ... films ... beer although trying the wine but not quite there yet ... sitting out on the patio and enjoying the views with more beer ... I work for a local firm as a manager and usually have a lot of free time on evenings to hang out with friends and family.

I have a Degree from my University days during the early 90's in Leeds ... Probably the best years so far for me ... This year Im looking to at least match those times and hopefully meet new people and get sheetfaced!

So drop me an email and who knows ...

Great someone that hasn't enjoyed themselves in over a decade, owns a cat, lives on a hill and is clearly an alcoholic. BINGO! Saying that, he is the right height and does have hair...Is it time to compromise?

For Fun: Well lets see ... Im 32, live all by lonesome in my man-pad ...have a good career in retail management ... got a degree ...

can fly aeroplanes although have trouble with my VW sometimes ... I like keeping fit and Hellmans mayonaisse on everything!

My Job: **Work for a small/medium sized retailer as a branch manager ... really just sit about all day looking important and doing not very much**

My Ethnicity: **I is white ...**

My Religion: **Non church going Catholic**

Favorite Hot Spots: **Go out in Leeds usually every 2 weeks or so... End up in one of the clubs around the area to go shaking my tush ... oh and say hello to the ladies and Jack Daniels who Im close friends with =)**

Favorite Things: **Favs = Pasta ... Bottoms ... Brunettes & Blondes ... French Blue ... Friends ... JD & Coke ... Sleeping ... Flying ... Hiking ... Pubs ... Cats ... House Music ... Shawshank Redemption ... Golf ... typing dots ...**

I rest my case.

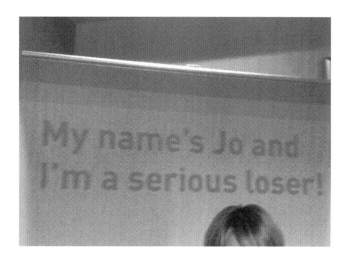

This is the helpful sign I have to walk
past in my local gym every single day

Apathetic April

It's now Easter. "What?" I hear you cry. Yes I'm afraid it's true, time flies. I don't know where it's gone but gone it has. Admittedly my subscriptions expired so it's time to renew and view the messages I've been receiving but could not access without paying. Let's see what we've got.

Message From: Craig

hi,

Call me bolshy by all means, but why do you say that it is important for everyone to be close to their family?

I understand that you are close to your family, but you must accept that the closeness of other people to their families will be based on the net effect of a completely different upbringing and life to yours. Hence, to expect others to feel exactly the same way as you, based upon completely different experience and context, is illogical. Unless, by implication you are saying that you wish to filter out anybody who does not have an identical background?

Sorry to be blunt but several people have said the same thing and it strikes me as unreasonable.

It is the same as me saying I am Aquarius, therefore everybody else should be also, regardless of when they were born.

Anyway, I will, get off my soap box now and do something constructive. Why do I always get into these conversations? No offence. Have a nice life and so forth. Apologies for any inconvenience. Normal service will resume shortly. Stick me in your next comedy script as Mr A. Rant of Norfolk.

thanks, Craig

Obviously, I have to say, a little disappointing. I wasn't expecting the first message I read to be frankly argumentative and slightly aggressive. In fact I felt quite aggrieved, so much so that I actually went back and looked at my profile to check what I'd written.

"YOU ABSOLUTELY MUST WITHOUT EXCEPTION, EVEN IF YOUR PARENTS BEAT YOU ENDLESSLY WITH AN ANVIL AND KEPT YOU IN THE ATTIC FEEDING YOU NOTHING BUT COAL AND WORMS, YOU MUST, I REPEAT MUST, BE CLOSE TO THEM, LOVE THEM AND SPEND EVERY WEEKEND WITH THEM BRINGING THEM GIFTS OF CHOCOLATE AND WINE".

Thankfully I said nothing of the sort. What I DID say was that to me it's important that *I* am close to *my* family and don't get me wrong but I think perhaps this chap just possibly MAY have had an unfortunate childhood. However, the good news is that it appears not to have affected him at all. Honestly, as if I don't have enough daily grief without complete strangers reprimanding me by email about something I didn't even say. Life is weird. I've just realised he's from Norfolk so perhaps he took umbrage thinking I was being sarcastic about the fact his mother is really his sister and his wife is his mum's daughter and his dad is his nan's grandson!

Message From Dan:

Hi Jo,

I'm Dan from London (Hertfordhsire/Berkshire/Bucks area). Hope you don't mind me sending you a message, but I read your profile and you sound like a really nice person who is easy going and relaxed. I like someone who has a good sense of humour and likes to take life as it comes. I'm looking to make friends and see what happens. By the way I'm 6ft tall, 13 stone, 42 Chest, 32 Waist, Muscular/Toned build, Brown/Hazel eyes and Short Dark Hair. I'm told I'm attractive (and not just by my mother) no point lieing!!! Unfortunately my pic wont load not sure why and my pic is a little fuzzy. If you want my pic I couild send it via my cam fone. If you text me or let me have your number only if you feel comfortable.

My father is from Singapore and my mother from England and I was born in Manchester but now I am down South.

I enjoy going to the Gym regularly and playing sports rather than watching, sorry but I don't like watching sports (not a football fan!). I am a very sporty and active. But do enjoy parties, wine bars, nice pubs salsa dancing all kinds of music and of course holidays!!!

I am single with no children.

I work as a senior manager for blue-chip company nr London.

Anyway I would love to hear from you would be good, you could always text me I don't bite honest!!! Nothing ventured nothing gained so they say, sometimes you just have to look for the stars and have a go - are you up for it! I do hope so - just as scary for me you know.

If you like my profile and would like to speak to me then please feel free to text or fone me. Unfortunately I don't access my email very often once every 2 weeks or so.

I am on a 3 day trialy. After you will have to email me or use my mobile.

Well take care and best wishes

Dan

Oh dear, doesn't look like I've missed much so far. Yet another "you look/sound/hopefully are a nice person" email. What can a girl do? My first questions would be:

a) Are you a cheapskate signing up for the lowest subscription and then bulk emailing anyone who looks vaguely female with your real contact details?

b) Why was internet dating your preferred way of meeting someone when you admit to not checking your emails regularly?

I smell a rat! NB Mister, I'm not your tailor so please don't furnish me with your measurements. How rude.

Message From Frank:

Hi Jo,

Well - You have in fact won the booby prize - a message from me !!!! ;-)

Aaaaaaaaanway... Woweee!!!! What a nice profile :-) Just came across your profile while "looking" around and thought your picture and your personal description were spot on :-) And distance is not a problem, hence me dropping you a line.

If you want to have a look at my profile and drop me a line that would be great... and let's see where we can go from there.

Hope to hear from you... Frank

Frank. Can I be frank? Anyone who puts "distance is not a problem" when they also live in London is frankly, Frank, rubbish! Also, Frank, can I be frank for the last time? If tonight, Matthew/Harry Hill ... Frank is going to be thirty-five, then also, Matthew/Harry ... for one night only ... Jo is going to be twenty-one.

Message From Sam:

Hi Jo,

nice profile

have a good weekend

Now what exactly am I supposed to do with this? I could reply "Ditto have a nice life". Let's look at his profile:

More about Sam and what he is looking for:

I dont want a short term meaningless relationship unless your very attractive and have the morals of a goat.Im looking for a longer term. I would hope if I meet that special person we don't discuss who keeps what, until at least 15yrs after meet up.If you have kids so what I'm 41 and a realist. If 2.4 more kids come along and two dogs by the seaside even better (you walk the dogs).Forget the seaside I work in London and the dogs could be a pain if we both work all day.I'm a normal guy wont hide my home nos after a few dates and wont bring wedding photos or my mother on the first date.

If you want a drop dead gorgeous guy im not it. However lets face it such guys are usually gay ,dont phone back ,lie or cant use a fork or knife without training ! I've also done the usual stuff ski- ing, scuba diving + travelling like dancing (Jive ceroc etc.)own my own home and even occassionally phone my mother ! And Im just 6 1 not 6 4 !. Ps if your looking for a DVD red bottle of wine and the guy must have a sense of humour , you can get two from tesco and the third from me ! pps 'looking for a woman who won't hit me, esp. on the arm when I pick my food up on with the knife!'.It was a mistake !

Well he's certainly more verbose when talking about something he's interested in. Himself. Although I have to say that judging by his photo, he's quite obviously not my type. I'm quite impressed with his approach. He's the first guy that, instead of selling himself, has decided the best form of defense is to attack the opposition. I do suspect that, if and when he meets any potential ladies from the site who don't return his interest, he'll immediately tar them with the lesbian brush.

Message From Riccardo:

Hi Jo,

I am a friend of riccardo .....I relly like to see you ...your profile is very intereresting ....write to me ...ciao Raniero

OK now this is a first. I'm now getting messages from the friends of people I don't want to see! No one tells you about this when you subscribe. Just looked at Riccardo's profile and he looks very, shall we say, "intense" in his photo. I'll let his profile speak for itself ...

More about Riccardo and what he is looking for:

I believe that describing my own personality take some interest away from who can be possibly interested in me. If anyone wishes to know my profile can still ask for it. The one thing I can say about my character is what I always look to find in a person: Spontaneity and creativity. If you have these two qualities, I will be so interested in you.

I think the only spontaneous thing anyone who views your profile will do is hit the Delete button. But wait, it isn't even Riccardo who is pursuing me. No. It's Raniero, the tight-arsed friend of an intense-looking, arrogant bloke who knows enough about himself to wisely not describe himself for fear of not being interesting.

Message From Luke:

Hi Jo,

Hope you are well and getting a good response. I liked your profile and you look great too.

It would be good to find out more about you. Do you have a favourite spot for a night out?

How long have you been a struggling actor and have you had any unusual parts?

What music are you listening to at the moment?

Take a look at my profile and hopefully you will see some similar interests that we can explore further.

Maybe we can chat, see if we click and then see what happens...

Looking forward to hearing from you. Luke

Luke, you know, I know it, we ALL know it - it will never, could never work. YOU ARE GINGER! Not even auburn, or strawberry blonde. You are the gingeriest ginger I have seen in a long time. Our children would be scary and you'd have to either shave your head or wear hats for the duration of our relationship. I've also just noticed you're also five foot five. I simply cannot tolerate such an abomination.

Message From Ben:

Hi Jo, how are you today, I hope live is going OK with you, will be nice if I hear from you. Take care

This guy looks like an overweight David Baddiel with Mr Magoo glasses ...

More about Ben and what he is looking for:

I am a father to 3 beautiful daughters which I miss allot, at present single and is killing me, I decided to join this dating staff and I am all new to this so girls be easy with me, I describe my self a loving living sole like Garfield, so girls if you love Garfield then do not look any further, also I consider my self caring/honest/trust worthy/ helpful/faithful toward life and very hopeful, Like to be very private with my life only share my secrets with the right half, I thing this is good and the best I could come up with so far.

I do have a few sport activities and hobbies also I love going to the gym to stay active, like to travel and meet other peoples from all kinds, as I do like to understand and knowing all cultures from around the globe, I enjoy eating out very much specially romantic diners I just love them, and I do love flowers very much as they do bright my life/ I like to music such as Jazz, Soul, Classic & Country Music/pop,do not Like Hard Rock. Any way I'm trying my best to do a good profile her and to make sure is not boring, please try to give me some credit here for this as some did not.

Now, I'm inclined to go "ahhhhhhh" when I read this. I was, as you know, by now hoping for much greater things. Alas, the reality, like most things in life, is ever so slightly disappointing. Most unnervingly they've now moved on from living with/loving their cats to actually thinking they are a cat and, even worse, GARFIELD! Let's read more.

About Ben:

Family Status: **Divorced**

Sexuality: **Straight**

Children: **3+**

Education: **College**

Profession: **Other**

Religion: **Other**

Employment: **Employed**

Practising (religion): **Non Practising**

Income: **Moderate**

Star Sign: **Capricorn**

Race: **Other**

Eye Colour: **Hazel**

Height: **5'9" - 6' (1.71m - 1.80m)**

Hair Colour: **Black**

Build: **Average / Medium**

Hair Length: **Short**

Appearance: **Average**

Facial Hair: **Clean Shaven**

One thing we do have in common is a love of fresh flowers as I too believe they "bright my life" and I do also like "to music" just not with a forty-year old divorcee with 3+ children who thinks he's a cat. Anyway what the hell does: 3+ children mean? That's what it actually states, but he only mentions three in his profile so does that mean he has someone up the duff somewhere and yet is still trying to flirt via the internet?

Message From Ben:

Hi Jo,sorry for the spelling mistake

See, I told you he was an "aahhhh bless". He sent another email apologising for a spelling mistake. Not all of my cold heart can have turned to stone. You'll have noticed I didn't even pick on his spelling and grammar.

Message From Marc:

Hi Jo,

Hello,....Your profile got my attention...you sound interesting, and I thought I'd send you a message...the pic's not to bad either!!

How's your weekend been?...what did you get up to?...I went out in the west end - company paid :)...im an estate agent by the way.

If you want to chat...msg me back!! Marc

Cheeky sod. More than I can say for your photo my dear. When trying to grab a girl's attention I wouldn't recommend pointing out that you're not only tight but, even worse, an estate agent. Marc, you are the weakest link... GOODBYE!

Message From Nick:

Hi Jo,

So you're still on here... did you find anyone who could arrive on time?

I think it's a conspiracy to wind me up. This is from the guy who told me he was running late at the time he was scheduled to meet me. The Lisping Policeman. Well Mr, as is blatantly obvious, yep I am STILL on here. Although I should point out very obviously SO ARE YOU! LET IT GO! STEP AWAY FROM THE COMPUTER. THERE'S NOTHING TO SEE HERE!

ARRGGHHHHHHHHHHHHHHHHHHHHHHHHHHHHHHHHHHHH. Most annoying though is the fact the he knows that I seem to be incapable of meeting anyone. I suppose when you log off for a while everyone presumes you are missing "happy" not missing "too skint" to re-subscribe.

Message From Joe:

Hi Jo,

Hmmmmmm. Good tactic. Less is more. Let's see what he has to say and looks like ... okay so may be not so good.

More about Joe and what he is looking for:

I,m geneguse ,romantic ,emotional,caring,responsible,hard working,at the same time ,believing in moderation in life. I believe also that relation is a construction .We built it during the time of relationship positively. not before...

I can see why he's a man of few words.

Message From Raj:

Hi Jo,

No auditions today then? :o)

Is there anyone out there not trying to piss me off? Even strangers are goading me.

More about Raj and what he is looking for:

Unconventional & articulate, I've left the Rat Race to pursue a career in Photography(I've already exhibited).Chic & trendy bars don't impress me, LESS so try-hard "Hot London Chicas".The sort of woman I'm looking for would NOT be a Home Counties cliche:a Lucy/Charlotte/Jessica who lives in the SWs (Clapham/Wandsworth uber alles!), works in Marketing/PR/Whatever, has a "great bunch of friends but is missing that something/someone special","is up for anything once", has done "Machu Pichu/Angkor/scuba diving off the Reef/bungee jumped" (yawn) I guess that rules most of you out.If you're strong,level-headed,very bright, and classy you're my type. I DO have a pic however, anyone rightaway asking for it rightaway earns an all-expenses paid, one-way ticket to my Ignore List.You've read the profile and are probably wondering, "who is this t*sser?" but hey, if you've come this far and, if the profile was incendiary enough to scorch your chic Brazilian then you're interested, right?:o)

Raj, to use your own words, "who is this tosser?" And more importantly "why is he emailing me?" WHY? Just to be clear, I did not and have never e-mailed Raj although the manner of his initial email would lead you, dear reader, to assume that I had contacted him.

Am I Alone in Noticing these?

41. You have no idea who is Number One in the charts.

42. Hairy bum! (not on the outside thankfully) but when did that happen?

43. You secretly wish mobile phones were simply phones and have no idea how to use any of the other functions you paid dearly for.

44. You now complain about bad service and have even complained about how the complaint's been dealt with.

45. All your favourite films are still on VHS.

46. In your head you still buy and eat Marathons and Opal Fruits.

47. You only buy a paper if there's a free DVD or CD enclosed.

48. You secretly buy and enjoy reading "Heat" magazine. But only at the checkout or dentist. You'd never actually pay for it.

49. Bingo IS an option!

50. Okay so you squint a lot, get a few headaches and your arms aren't long enough to read anything anymore. Doesn't *necessarily* mean you need glasses.

SINGLES LOG: DATE NUMBER FIVE

Queen B

We'd arranged to meet outside the Dominion Theatre. I had a casting and had previously warned him they have no concept of time so could well be delayed. He was fine about it which was good. When I finally left the casting, which was about a two minute walk from the Dominion, I saw the guy I was meant to be meeting hanging around outside the theatre. I recognised him, but he looked one hell of a lot older. He hadn't spotted me so - and I know this is a terrible thing - I walked straight past and kept on walking. I felt guilty. After all, he had been patient. But I just knew it would be pointless. I didn't get very far before he called my mobile. I looked at his name on my phone and guilt took over so I answered. I told him I'd just left and would be there in two minutes. I hate that about me. I readily criticise people with no morals or conscience but the truth is I really REALLY wish I didn't have any. Life would be so much easier.

So we walk to an All Bar One round the corner. He does buy the drinks and we sit and chat. He had said he's a singer in a band - I'd had delusions of fame as a singer/songwriter in my youth so I thought we might be suited. That was, of course, before I saw him. When I ask him about his band he seems cagey. Then eventually he confesses: he was, in fact, the lead singer in a Queen tribute band! That's right, I'm sitting having a drink with a Freddie Mercury look-alike. Strangely though, he doesn't actually look like him at all, until he produces photos of their gigs and then it's really quite uncanny.

We then talk about past relationships, during which he openly admits that the reason he left his last girlfriend (of eight years) was because she wanted to get married and have children. Hmmm, not entirely unreasonable of her, don't you think? As we talk it becomes clear that he doesn't want to meet someone else. He's still in love with his ex and he regrets leaving her. I think I successfully make him realise that marriage and kids are what most women want at some point in a relationship. I basically tell him that even if he meets someone new, it's highly likely that they, too, after a certain amount of time will probably want those things.

I don't get men at all. Why do they all seem to want to remain single or hang desperately on to the illusion of being single even when they've lived with their partner for x amount of years? It's bizarre. Why does gaining a wife and eventually, if you're lucky, having kids feel to them like losing something? Perhaps it feels that way for some women too? Maybe I'll never know. He had a good thing going and I think he realised that talking to me. It makes no sense to throw away with both hands something good, only to be left trawling through the internet looking for exactly what you had. I hope he gets back with her and they get married and live happily ever after. Anyway, anyone who's happy to marry and have kids with an aging rocker who makes a living performing as a gay icon should be snapped up. Perhaps I should be a relationship counsellor? *Who are you kidding? You're hardly a success story.* It's unfortunately always easy to see things more clearly when you're not involved. Giving advice is easy.

dose of caffeine, sodium glycerophosphate, dipotassium phosphate and disodium phosphate to Christ's bloodstream. This causes Jesus to 'go radge' up in Heaven, attacking new arrivals asking for his autograph by melting them with his eyes, responding to prayers with expletive-ridden rants and staggering around completely nude in visions.

 TAURUS 21 APR – 21 MAY You feel like an insignificant pube fallen among the wheels of a large machine whose action you do not understand but which is working well.

GEMINI 22 MAY – 21 JUN The mind of Gemini is like a toilet U-bend. It needs to flow. If a particularly big brown thought gets stuck, only the rubber gloves of truth can dislodge

I can confirm I am Taurus

May Hem

It's my birthday so I'm now 34. THIRTY-FOUR! How the hell did that happen? Okay I kind of knew it was coming (after all I was 33 for a year) but I mean give me a break. My mum isn't even here. She's in Australia for a month. Yep, that's right - my sixty-six year old mum with two new titanium hips is gadding about in a country I've always longed to visit. To rub the salt in, from where in Australia does she ring me? The SYDNEY OPERA HOUSE! So let's recap: I'm a single, thirty -fo..something year old and it's my birthday and where am I? At home. What am I doing? Getting ready to go out. And where am I going? TO WORK! Where did I go so terribly wrong? There must something to cheer me up ...

42-year-old man

seeking women 25-45

About me and what I'm looking for:

i love old fashioned but stylish people and things, because i am that way myself . i think i'm very attractive(i've made the effort) i love meeting interesting people. i have always been unorthodox in my approach to life, never fitted into any recognised way of life. i can be passionate about people and things that i love. i have practised at the english bar for some years while leading a jazzband playing american popular music of the 1920s, 30s, and 40s.

looking for someone attractive, intelligent, talented(artistic), interested in old-fashioned but stylish pastimes(i know i'm using a computer) i'm willing to share other interests with the right person. i am deeply suspicious of people with extreme views on anything(esp. religion and race) i can be fiercely loyal when i get to know and care for someone. i always love the thrill of starting an affair and i am open to much more besides...and i'm sorry, but i'm not looking for a pen pal..i don't care what any american dating 'experts' say about meeting/getting to know your ideal partner online.i don't think i can, and if you can, you're a better man than i...looking forward to genuine replies.

I do like a chap who knows when he's using a computer! Bit too honest telling a potential partner how much you "love the thrill of starting an affair". Slightly concerned that he thinks I'm a better "man" than he is!!!!

From: Derek:

Hi

My name is Derek and I live and work in Croydon. I live in my own house with a cat called Tabitha.

My interests range from science fiction to medieval history. I like to read, watch TV, go to the theatre and the cinema and to go out to eat and drink (not necessarily in that order).

I enjoy cooking, especially big meals for lots of people, but I can do romantic dinners for two as well.

I like the countryside, in the summer I enjoy visiting village pubs for a pint and a ploughman's.

I am quite well travelled but my travels have been closer to home since I got a mortgage.

I enjoy going out, but miss having someone to go out with.

I would love to hear from you. Derek

Sounds familiar? I know. Quite clearly after four months on the site Derek still hasn't met Ms Right. Mind you it might help if he remembered who he'd already emailed. Let's see though in four months how his life's changed. Tabitha has moved up the pecking order and is promoted to the second sentence from third. Good to see Derek's still your man if you fancy a ploughmans! Science fiction and medieval history are new strings to his bow. Glad to see he's not wasted those four months. I don't know why I'm finding this so funny? I'm still looking too and have no new skills to show for all that time. Perhaps another quick search on some others is in order:

More about Jules and what he is looking for:

I`m a natural thinker,and I almost analize everything around me, if you are looking for "somebody that will make you laugh" you better skip to the next profile.I don`t like croudy and noisy places(butI can sacrifice occasionally).I like the outdoor,nature,and a nice conversation.I`m looking for somebody who is interested mainly in genuine relationship rather then standard target like"marriage"or "joint bank account".If you think you are ready to start something without shape or definition, well.. just give me a shout(loud).

Jules, at your request I shall skip to the next profile as I really would rather like someone who will make me laugh. And don't put yourself down. You really are much funnier than you give yourself credit for!

More about Mitch and what he is looking for:

i'm laid back very easy going , like to meet a woman who is non vegataian, not into cats & salsa dancing, must be some woman over 35 thats not into these, though very hard to find

Do you want the good news or the bad news, Mitch? The good news is, although I don't dislike cats, I wouldn't say I am particularly "into" them - the same goes for salsa dancing. The bad news is I'm thankfully not yet over thirty-five. Good luck searching. I sympathise. It's not easy I know!

37-year-old man

seeking women 32-39

Relationships: **Divorced**

Have kids: **None**

Want kids: **Definitely (2)**

Ethnicity: **White / Caucasian**

Body type: **About average**

Height: **6'1" (185.4cms)**

Religion: **[No Answer]**

Smoke: **No Way**

Drink: **Social drinker, maybe one or two**

About me and what I'm looking for:

Honestly - this process Sure Uncovers Xenophobics. But I will not give in.

My close friends describe me as a having a strong charactor, a quietly spoken thinker who is capable of achieving much while maintaining a down to earth nature. I am not afraid to take steps in directions less travelled and in some cases reap the rewards and in others gained invaluable experiences. Those friends whose judgement I respect most have complemented me on having a global view on the world and an ability to broaden their own views or thinkings.

My lifestyle allows me to work and travel with a lot of flexability. My plan is to continue this until I either find a great place to settle permanently or I find a girl to settle permanently with in which case it becomes a joint decision. Luckily here, I can adapt to pretty much any environment but I have a preference for spending time in S.E. England (Cardiff n Edinburgh are OK also), the Nordics or Australia. Ideally, you also have a lifestyle and drive to enable us to alternate between work, family and personal time. Realisticaly, you are past the 'me' stage in life and ready to commit to something serious.

When in relationships, I enjoy the together things like maintaining the house, routine shopping, planning the garden, entertaining etc. This is normal for me and although the single life gives me opportunity to go my own path, I feel something missing.

I have no preconceived ideas or a checklist to match you against. Previously I have fallen head over heals for professionals as easily as general workers. Even though some have had significantly different backgrounds, they they all had a common sence of purity, honesty, openess and a sence of adventure.

This is what I seek.

Let's examine his first sentence. Why has he chosen to use capitals? Is it a code, and what he's really saying is "This process SUX", in which case I'm in full agreement. A guy that unnecessarily used the word "xenophobic" and spelt it correctly, to then misspell simple words like "character" and "flexibility", surely should arouse suspicion? A tad patronising about how very enlightening and inspiring he is to all his alleged "friends". Actually, just re- read that and it's only the friends "whose judgment I respect" who say that about him. Strange to have friends you don't respect but to be fair he does respect "most" of them. Nope, out of all my friends I can honestly say there's not one of them whose judgment I don't respect. Be nice to hear what the friends he doesn't respect have to say about him. As for "past the ME stage" I think he very much wants his next partner to be into the 'him' stage and nothing else.

Wow how exciting is he? He enjoys "maintaining the house and shopping". What a barrel fit to burst of laughs is he? They are CHORES, not fun. Necessities - things that HAVE to be done. It is, however, reassuring that he'd stoop low enough to have a relationship with a "general worker". I can hear the excited giggles of female "general workers" everywhere. You keep seeking, mate, we'll keep hiding ...

34-year-old man

seeking women 25-38

Relationships: **Never Married**

Have kids: **None**

Want kids: **Someday (2)**

Ethnicity: **White / Caucasian**

Body type: **Slender**

Height: **5'8" (172.7cms)**

Religion: **Christian / Protestant**

Smoke: **No Way**

Drink: **Social drinker, maybe one or two**

About me and what I'm looking for:

I'm quiet, shy, thoughtful, intelligent, principled, faithful, spiritual, a serious but questioning Christian, poor but interested in things, a good teacher and a published writer. I'm selective in my friends. I'm often amused, and sometimes depressed. Work, prayer and star-gazing keep me sane. Lies, laziness and littering make me angry. I have three left feet and an addiction to garlic, and I'm still searching for the ultimate way to clean colanders. Do we have anything in common? If so, get in touch!

This guy didn't mail me, I just happened upon his profile. Do you think I should email him and tell him garlic addiction, having an extra foot (all left), being depressed and admitting to being a colander obsessive do not a great date make? No. He'll find out the hard way.

Just thinking. Do I have any bizarre addictions or phobias? Well I didn't feel it necessary to put it on my profile, but I do actually have a thing about buttons. A "thing" as in I'm scared of them. Well not so much scared, more I don't trust them - they make me feel sick and I can't touch them. Especially those clear or white shirt buttons! Horrible. I guess it's a bit of luck I've never been approached by a pearly king or queen. I know it sounds weird but it's a real phobia. Covered buttons or metal ones on jeans and denim are fine. You don't believe me do you? Look:

Using hypnotherapy to treat button phobia.

Button Phobia

Button phobia is surprisingly common.

Often, sufferers are surprised to learn that they are far from alone in this surprisingly common, although often unspoken, phobia.

The sufferer quite often believes that they are 'the only one' to suffer from this phobia.

Sufferers often report:

- The fear depends on the type or size of button

- The fear may only come when the button has 'come loose'

- The noise that buttons make may bring a panic attack

- The fear may have started in early childhood

- The inability to make contact with others wearing buttons

- The need to choose clothes for their children that use zips, metal fasteners, elastic or velcro

- They can't say, write, or type the word 'buttons'

- Male sufferers often find it especially difficult if they work in an office, because they don't like to wear standard office clothing.

- They may be afraid of breathing in near a button, in case they inhale the button

If you suffer with button phobia, don't suffer in silence, contact us straight away for a hypnotherapy for phobias appointment.

We'll be pleased to meet you, listen to you, and start the process of using hypnosis to treat that annoying phobic anxiety.

See? I told you. I can confirm I don't possess any items of clothing or soft furnishings with the particular type of button I can't stand. I've had issues during moments of passion with men wearing shirts that have been most inconvenient. As the astute among you will have already noticed, I can type the word "button" so I'm clearly not an emergency case. I love the fact that they take us "button phobics" so seriously. I wish they did TV and radio ads "Don't suffer in silence". Hysterical. You are without doubt by now screaming at this page "YOU HYPOCRITE". And well you should. Yes I do have a peculiar phobia and yes it could be equated to being similar in phobia-ness to a previous boyfriend who shall remain nameless. Correct. I should point out however, just like said boyfriend who had his phobia for many years, I too have had this since the age of around four or five. I have not and would never suggest to a boyfriend (if I had one) that I should spend the whole of our first Valentine's weekend in a hotel with other button sufferers. No, I still claim we should have spent that weekend with his bladder fit to burst and me gingerly and, perhaps with the aid of marigolds, sexily trying get his shirt off!

Surely there simply can't be any more?

51. You're over the moon with the new Dr Who series and remember it first time round. But you thought David Tennant was best.

52. You have all the Weight Watchers literature gathering dust in a cupboard somewhere.

53. You wouldn't consider going to the cinema any other day than "Orange Wednesday".

54. You'd rather stay sober and drive than pay for expensive cabs.

55. Manners have become very important to you and a lack of them is very distressing.

56. You realise your mum was married and had all her children by the time she was your age.

57. You have at least one direct debit for a charity.

58. When you're referred to as Mrs in shops or on the phone it sends chills down your spine but you never correct them.

59. Forty doesn't seem so old.

60. You've tried using haemorrhoid cream on your eye bags.

Right. This is it. The end of my subscriptions. I signed up initially for a month on two sites and then got carried away. The facts:

I was viewed 1944 times. Mostly by bald pensioners with personality disorders and cats.

I received well over a hundred emails, again mostly from people falling into the above category.

I sent 57 emails/winks. None of the ones I liked replied.

I went on approx 15 dates, the most memorable of which I have described.

I'm still single and although I know this method works for some people I've discovered it's not for me. I have to admit it's been fun in a way - quite different to expectations. The truth is, you never know, and if you like vertically challenged, bald men with cats, well knock yourself out!

SINGLES LOG: DATE NUMBER SIX

The City Slicker Reiki Healer

We agree to meet at Café Rouge close to where we both live. I arrive and he's already seated. To my surprise he actually resembles his photo and looks quite nice. Hurray. He's bought a bottle of white and has an extra glass so pours me one. Excellent. We start chatting. He proceeds to tell me continuously how much money he has. He also produces not one but three business cards: His Investment Banker one, his Reiki Healer one and lastly his Psychoanalyst one. Hmmmmm. It becomes clear during our conversation that we disagree on most important issues. I'm also becoming increasingly disturbed by his ever increasingly erratic behaviour. He seems to get extremely tense, dare I say, enraged, when I challenge his views.

The waitress comes over and I tell her we are not eating. He looks surprised so I say we're clearly not compatible and that it's probably best if we drink up and leave. He however changes tack and says that he likes me and the fact that I'm "challenging". I want to go home but can see I'm not going to escape easily. I steer the conversation away from potential hot potatoes and on to more personal details like, does he have brothers and sisters, etc. This unbeknownst to me opens up a whole tin kettle of fishy worms. What could possibly be wrong with this topic of conversation I hear you cry? Wait for it...HE'S ADOPTED!

"NOOOOOOOOOOOOOOOOOOOOOOOOO".

"OH YES HE IS. WHAT HAVE I DONE?"

I'm struck dumb and it takes what seems like ages for me to muster "That must have been difficult for you". What else could I, should I say? He was already quite frightening company. It's typical that when trying to choose a less challenging subject, the one I thought would be most harmless, e.g. family, should be one that adds fuel to a frankly already roaring fire!

He's clearly agitated, he leans into me and says quite threateningly "I don't want your pity". HELP! He calms down and tells me about his childhood and after each story finishes by saying "But I've dealt with that now". He doesn't look or behave like someone who has "dealt with it" at all. I mistakenly ask him if he thought the reason he feels the need to overachieve and help people with Reiki and his Psychoanalysis is, in fact, purely because despite saying he's dealt with his past he in fact hasn't? I didn't mean to light the fire and I realise now the above comment could be seen as fanning the flames but, believe me, it was a genuine reaction to a clearly mixed-up guy. Added to his already somewhat strange mannerisms, he now clasps his wine glass so hard I fear it's going to smash and he's trembling. "Don't try your amateur psychology on me" he snarls. I promptly catch the waitress's eye for the bill. Thankfully it's not busy and she brings it almost immediately. He insists on paying and I practically run to my car. Sixth time's a charm! Way to go.

What scares me the most though is that you, as I, probably incorrectly, assume that if you're unfortunate enough to need a psychoanalyst that they, of all people, would be sane, stable, rational human beings ...

Apparently there were more:

61. When you finally get round to shaving your legs you lose two pounds in weight.

62. You don't just have a "muffin top" but also "muffin thighs" (especially when wearing hold ups - v. sexy!)

63. You wear comfy tracky bottoms (allegedly just around the house).

64. You have two sets of jeans: 1. a fat set & 2. a less fat set. Currently you can't manoeuvre yourself into either.

65. A nice cup of tea tops and tails the beginning and end of your day.

66. You dread making the effort to go to parties etc. and when you do you spend the whole time looking forward to getting home.

67. All your friends actually think you like being single and pretend to envy you.

68. Holidays. No fun on your own and the middle bit between your shoulders and back always burns. Just how do you apply lotion to that spot on your own?

69. The only blowing you have done recently was blowing the gathering dust off that unused, out of date box of condoms.

70. All your ex-boyfriends are engaged, married or having babies.

71. You're starting to consider cosmetic surgery, for example, enlarging your breasts and lips whilst reducing your stomach, thighs and arse.

72. Your next holiday is likely to be a yoga retreat. However, you suspect your holiday companions will mainly consist of menopausal women and womanopausal (that surely is the correct term for the male version?) men that had a mental

breakdown. The yoga teacher will definitely speak in that slow calm tone that bugs you to the point where you'd like to snap her in half. Of course you couldn't. She'd just frigging bend.

73. You start to think maybe blondes do have more fun and dye your once dark healthy hair so it now resembles a blonde brillo pad.

74. You really and truly do hope it's like riding a bicycle and fear that should you eventually meet someone you may have to purchase stabilisers.

75. Your electric blanket, or "Ed Blanque" as you refer to him, is the only thing that will be keeping you warm in bed this winter.

76. Your friends' sons are starting to look vaguely attractive.

77. On your work Christmas party invite they no longer bother to put "and guest".

78. You read a Feng Shui book and very promptly move your bed from under the window. In the vain hope it will make a difference.

79. Nice guys you meet even in their early twenties are already married! Leaving you wondering why every boyfriend you've ever had has been such a marriage/commitment-phobe?

80. The Pill part deux - surplus to requirements but you know 100% that when you tell your doctor you wish to come off it he'll look at your age, nod knowingly and say "trying for a baby?"

ARRRGGGGGHHHHHHHHHHHHHHHHHHHHHHHHHH!

SINGLES LOG: DATE NUMBER SEVEN

Lucky Number 7

Right if you fall off the horse it's best to get back on immediately isn't it? That's what they say anyway. So undeterred, or should I say undisturbed, I forge ahead. This chap seems lovely and he lives less than a mile away too. We share a love of comedy and tennis. He's a successful entrepreneur with too much time on his hands and looking for his next project. He thinks it might be me. Cheesy I know but what the hell, let's meet up. Oh BTW you may want to sit down. He is bald. Yup aha. Sexy bald. Not old man bald. See I'm not all bad. Here's how our date went:

We're sitting at a table and he's on his second large glass of port.

Him: I don't mean to go on about losing my parents it's just ...

My head: *No one will ever believe this is my real life.*

Me: It must be difficult.

Him: It's just that I feel I should be honest with you. I like you. I really do. But I'm an alcoholic ... the last time I saw my father ... I ... I hit him.

My head: *I don't know why restaurant chairs don't come with ejector seats. I have now officially entered the twilight dating zone.*

Me: Oh.

Him: I did love him.

Me: Of course you did.

(He starts scratching his arm.)

Me: Is your arm okay?

Him: I've got Ringworm.

Me: Ringworm!

My head: *Uncontrollable laughter - ask him if it's catching.*

Me: Is it…

Him: The Ugandan villagers in the orphanage I volunteered
                at recently gave it to me.

Me: How generous.

Him: Do you like me Jo? I want you to like me.

My head: *Are you quite mad? You're a self confessed violent alcoholic
                with ringworm.*

Me: To be honest, I think you're a lovely bloke …

Him: Really?

Me: But.

Him: I'm sorry, I didn't mean to ask you on a date to bring
                you down.

Me: No worries.

(Silence.)

Him: Let's go to a comedy club.

My head: *Sorry I understood I was already at one.*

Me: I don …

Him: I actually already booked tickets.

My head: *Still say no. Repeat after me. No No NO.*

Me: Sure.

My head: *You idiot! I am no longer conversing with you.*

(At the comedy club)

Him: He was brilliant huh? Just nipping to the toilet.

Me: Again?

Him: Won't be a tick.

(Whilst I'm sat on my own)

My head: *Considering freezing your eggs now aren't you?*

Me:	I just felt sorry for him. I've only lost one parent. I can't imagine how lonely it must feel when you eventually lose both, especially if you don't have a partner or family of your own.
My head:	*Would you listen to yourself? He's a complete disaster.*
Me:	He's lost both his parents.
My head:	*So have lots of people.*

(He returns with a blonde woman)

Him:	Talking to yourself? Could you move up one?
Me:	Ummmm. Sure.
Him:	Sue, this is Jo. Jo this is Sue. We met at the bar - she's a hoot. Jo is a big deal in the City, Sue.
Sue:	Oh really? What to do you do?
Me:	I don't. I'm not.
My head:	*LEAVE NOW. What's that white stuff under his nose?*
Me:	Listen, I've got to go now.
Him:	Oh okay. It's been a brilliant evening, thanks. I'll call you tomorrow.
Me:	Bye then. Good luck Sue.

It will come as no surprise to you that I didn't see him again. However I did hear from him. He rang me the next day three times. Of course I didn't answer so he left these messages …

Message One:

Hi Jo. I'm calling to apologise for my behaviour last night. Call me. Love you.

Message Two:

Jo. Me again. Listen, I was stupid. You are wonderful and I was an idiot. Please call me to let me apologise properly.

Message Three:

Jo I'm a complete arsehole. I shouldn't have done it and I apologise. I took Sue home. She's a lovely girl, fun, flirty - a lovely girl. We slept together and it was alright but I feel ashamed now and bad for you. I wanted it to be you. I was thinking of you. Love you. Bye. Call me.

Annus Horribilis

The Worst Things about being single:

Weddings

Weddings are a complete nightmare. Even more so in this day and age where they're so expensive your friends can't afford an extra hundred quid a head for an "and guest". Which is fair enough. Why should they want someone they barely know at their nuptials? Why indeed would I want someone I barely know and am not likely to see again to accompany me? I'll tell you why, because I guarantee EVERYONE will be with someone. As if that's not bad enough in every day life. The regular looks of pity from cousins, aunts, uncles etc. when they see you are on your own, yet again, at another family gathering. Being on your own at weddings is perhaps the most alone you can ever feel in a public place. The sheer tidal or, as I like to call it, "bridal wave" of knowing looks and "still not met Mr Right - oh dear never minds" you get are enough to make you look forward to happy family gatherings like a funeral where it is perfectly acceptable to be alone and crying. Also I'm willing to give a £100 prize to anyone who can explain to me just why I always get sat next to the twat in a kilt with glasses, skinny white legs and a borderline personality disorder? Anyone? No. Didn't think so.

Meeting new people

How many times have I and other single friends discussed the rudeness of people who have only just met you enquiring into your personal life? You start a new job and your colleagues enquire thusly:

Colleague:	Are you married?
Jo:	*No. I'm not sure I believe in it, actually.*
Colleague:	Oh! No boyfriend then?
Jo:	*Not at the moment, no, although I was with someone for ten years and we didn't feel the need to marry.*
Colleague:	Children?
Jo:	*No.*
Colleague:	Oh dear (pause as they scrutinise your wrinkles). Maybe soon hey?
Jo:	*No, actually, I'm not entirely sure I want any. Or if I'll ever meet someone I want to have them with.*
Colleague:	You'll change your mind. Fingers crossed for you. (knowing nod)

What makes these married forty-something women with their kids in day care so sure that I, or indeed anyone who may not want children, will change their minds? Who do they think they are? Why can't they mind their own bee's wax? More importantly, why do I/we reply so politely to such personal questions? From now on when anyone enquires I'll proudly announce the following:

"No, I'm not married, thank you for asking. I'm widowed. Sadly I can't have children. I was, in fact, born a man and am still recovering from surgical correction. I'm also, as you seem interested, a lesbian. Anything else you'd like to know?"

188

Pretending

The constant pretense that you like being single. I don't. I know some people claim to and I'm sure they actually do. But it's not for me. I, like my dear internet pal Derek, miss having someone to go out with and come home to. At least he has Tabitha! I do have my lovely dog Murphy but I really would like to go out with someone that doesn't insist on shitting in your garden, have bad breath or persistently licks his own balls. Sure I have lots of fabulous friends, but it's not the same. I miss not having someone to hold at night, to care about and who cares about me. Clearly looking for love doesn't work. I do wish, though, people would think about what they're saying when they constantly chant "Stop looking and it will happen when you least expect it". Oh really. I've been single and "not looking" for the past for three and half years and only finally met someone through speed dating (see first chapter) and a singles party. Neither of which were what you'd refer to as a success.

Men's Work

Despite our constant claims that we are all equal, we are not. I'm petrified by spiders no matter how small. I consider it a man's job to save me from their evil fangs and slow, slow, quick quick, slow leg movements. ARRRGGGGGGGGGHHHH. I can change light bulbs but when the one on the stairs goes I consider it too dangerous to balance on a step ladder at the top of the stairs. When I hear a noise at night it's not sufficient that I, a 5 foot 2 (I'm getting shorter as well as older), 9 stone girl, hair brush in hand, should quietly descend the stairs in order that, if being burgled, I can quickly but precisely coiffeur the burglar's hair and send them on their way! No, a naked man armed with a baseball bat is required in such circumstances. I can fill my tyres with air although I admit I just do it by sight, not properly with the gauge - but I cannot change a tyre. This again is man, boyfriend, husband, brother territory. The list is really endless so I shan't go on. Putting things up the loft or getting things down from the loft. Okay so I went on. Needless to say, there are things in this life that you just do need a man for. Really, despite the fact good ones are difficult to find and even the good ones can be a massive pain in the arse, they are in fact quite useful to have around.

Shaving

Ladies, please tell me I'm not the only single lady who, especially during the winter months, looks like she's grown a pair of trousers! It's sad to say that, when it's cold and you're living in trousers the majority of the time, if you took a peak at a single woman's legs you'd no doubt find them resembling two strips of Velcro. For some reason underarm hair is always well kept and of course the tash has to be kept at bay at all times. If I'm honest the bikini line comes and goes depending on what knickers I'm sporting that season. Of late I've been in favour of the lacy short variety. Which, although I find sexy and comfy, do encourage laziness in the waxing department. You can indeed get away with a multitude of pubic hair sins under those lovelies! In fact, I've been known to sport something not dissimilar to Mr Brian Blessed's face furniture.

Wearing Night Attire

Again, this is something I suspect all single males and females are guilty of - well, I'm hoping. I'd love to be one of those devil may care people who can sleep in the nude. However, as much as I try I simply cannot get a good night's rest when naked. So as a rule, when living or sleeping with a partner I have a selection of short sets and nighties - some cute, some sexy. However, when singledom descends on me I can guiltily hold my hands up to wearing the oldest, baggiest, most rotten, ill fitting t-shirts or pyjamas. Why is that? I suppose it just seems like a waste of time looking nice to go to bed alone. Although I have to say one of the guys I lived with had no shame. Constantly coming to bed wearing once white but now grey, bagging, sagging boxers complete with several fresh pee marks on the fly area. Most attractive.

Communication

Yes home phones, mobiles, email, Messenger, Skype, Facebook etc. are wonderful inventions. How did we ever get by without them? Well let me tell you, they're not so wonderful when you're single. When you have a boyfriend you get a little pang of excitement with every text tone and answer message bleep. Usually followed by opening a text that's full of "miss you's", "love you's" and "can't wait to see you's". You can see loved up people in all the usual places (trains, shops, friends having lunch with you who gave a number to a bloke the night before and whose eyes are glazing over as you speak) eagerly listening out for the tell tale beep, followed by a mad rummage for the phone, followed by a smile or smirk, followed by rushed keyboard dexterity, followed by the phone being set down or placed on their lap whilst they have a smug look on their faces. Then, beep, they get a reply and the cycle repeats. Phones, answerphones, texts, Messenger and emails etc. for the single person are all ways of making you feel totally unwanted. "You have no new messages", or you have logged on and are "receiving 8 new emails" - all which turn out to be spam.

Men in bars

Now you may think this is a foolish thing to add to my list considering that I suspect you may think this is the ideal scenario. You are mistaken. I was in a bar recently and actually to my surprise got chatting to a handsome, funny, tall guy. This seemed too good to be true so I asked him if he was married to which he replied "No". We chatted for quite some time and were clearly getting on well. At one point for some reason, and I can't honestly remember why, he grabbed my hands and made me feel his butt. I wasn't going to complain! Anyway about an hour later the he mentioned his girlfriend. I said "Excuse me?" He said with a Cheshire cat smile "You asked me if I was married". He clearly thought it not relevant to mention his poor girlfriend, with whom he's been living for three years and who, no doubt, would be delighted to know her boyfriend was in a bar making other women grab his arse! Honestly. This isn't the first time something similar to this has happened. They're everywhere - men who want it, all merrily flirting outrageously the moment their girlfriend's not in tow, leading many a single lady up the proverbial garden path.

Brothers

Another odd choice you may think? Well I have two and they couldn't be more different. One is married with three beautiful kids. The other has never been married and has three beautiful kids... all with different mothers! The non-married one is currently single again and, believe me, the way he behaves is enough to put you off men forever! He makes no bones about seeing several different women in the same week, sometimes in the same day. He forgets their names, forgets what he's said he's going to do with whom. Therefore, he'll often have seen the latest cinema release several times with different women. He has several "regular" ladies he sees. Although if you ask him which girlfriend he's seeing tonight he'll say he hasn't a single girlfriend let alone several. However, unfortunately for all of them they ALL think he is THEIR boyfriend! Ah, but your brother is probably a young whipper-snapper sowing his wild oats, in his prime. I regret to inform you he is forty-five!

Babies

My family and friends are of course aware that I'm single and have been for some time. So why do I often get asked when cuddling their children or playing with them "Ah look at you - getting broody" or "You'd make a wonderful mum"? How rude! Usually, I assure you, I'm not broody. I do however (not surprisingly) adore my nieces, nephews and friends' children. So why do people seem unable to understand the difference between A) playing with their kids for an hour or so and handing them back to B) gaining three stone, having feet and ankles the size of buses, obtaining piles, varicose veins and stretch marks, followed by a painful birth, a couple of weeks doing your best John Wayne impersonation, months of sleep deprivation and from then on a lifetime of worry! To me the difference there is not difficult to spot.

On the other hand, what if I *were* feeling "broody", eh? Well then in that case thanks very much. Cheers. Yeah, actually I am broody and would desperately love to have a child/children of my own now I'm older and more secure. However, can you spot the problem? Again, it's not a difficult one. Yes, that's right - I DON'T HAVE A BOYFRIEND! Let alone a husband. God damn it. In fact, think about it, I'm thirty-four so even if I do happen to meet a decent guy and we lived together for a couple of years blah blah - even if I met that guy tomorrow or this week or this year! - it's still frankly looking dicey for me now on the family front. So, parents everywhere, please, think twice before opening your traps. Unless of course I've missed the point and you're actually offering the services of your husbands, boyfriends, brothers?

Some of us may not be as lucky as you. Or some of us might; gasp, shock, horror simply not want to have kids through choice. Yes, it's true. It can happen. We're not all destined to be earth mothers. Those who choose not to have kids are sometimes referred to or thought of as selfish. Now I ask you, is it selfish to think this world's pretty shit, my life's not been great and why should I make some one else go through all this? There's so much war and what about global warming? Selfish pah!

Christmas & New Year

It's just awful. You dread it; the end of another year and STILL alone. You start every year with so much hope, only for it all to be dashed despite your valiant efforts to try and find a partner. Shamefully, you always manage to get all your cards written and posted about two weeks before Christmas because you have nothing better to do on those long, long winter evenings. Then every card that floats through your door is from a couple. You've given up going out on Christmas Eve - mainly because it involves paying a fortune to get into a bar you normally walk into for free, then spend the entire evening nose to nose with snogging couples or social misfits. No - Christmas Eve for you is putting your slippered feet up in front of the telly to find out the only film on is "Seven Feckin' Brides for Seven Feckin' Brothers". Actually, wait a minute, perhaps it's a subliminal message telling me what I really need to do to get someone to be my boyfriend is to break into their house, hit them on the head and kidnap them! Hmmmmm. Interesting thought and not something I will write off entirely. Christmas morning though is worse than the night before. Compared to an empty bed and no special surprises on Christmas morning "Bless Your Beautiful Hide" seems like seventh heaven as you make yourself a cup of tea and give your dog his present, half hoping he might have gone to the trouble of returning the favour. Sadly though, at the bottom of the stairs, bare foot, you tread in the only "little present" your dog ever leaves you. "MERRY CHRISTMAS"! It's really no surprise suicide rates quadruple over the "Festive Season".

I prefer the New Year to Christmas because although I seem to regularly find myself alone at this time of year, I'm still stupid enough to have hope. I naively look forward to the start of a New Year and look forward to putting the rubbish old one behind me. I spend time thinking of all the things I'm going to achieve in the forthcoming year and just how fantastic it's going to be and how I'll laugh at just how bad the year before was. Yeah right. I spent last New Year at a close friend's fancy dress party. I went dressed as a laughing policeman and thought it was hysterical. I nearly wet myself getting ready. I put the fat suit on first and couldn't see my feet to get my shoes on! Now, I love fancy dress parties but honestly, when am I going to get with the programme? Why do I always insist on hiring the funniest outfit? Every other woman in the room has the sense to look drop dead gorgeous dressed as the following; Marilyn Monroe, Cleopatra, Lara Croft, the list of beauties goes on.

So, basically, even if there were a single, good-looking, straight, emotionally stable, financially secure, intelligent man at the party looking for a long-term commitment, let's face it, he's not likely to be immediately drawn to a girl whose face is so red it looks like it's going to explode (owing to the heat contained within the fat suit), and who looks like she weighs thirty-four stone and keeps knocking drinks over with parts of her huge mass. Honestly, I never learn. The year before last I went to one dressed as Vicky Pollard, which again I thought was genius. Blonde wig, drawn on spots, awful tracksuit and a bit of padding topped off with lots of gold jewellery. Perfect. The main down side to this genius piece of fancy dressing was that sadly nobody thought I'd bothered with fancy dress!!!!! I give up.

Always look on the …

Ms Brightside

The Best Things about Being Single:

TV

Bliss. You're finally in complete charge of the remote. You can watch all manner of televisual rubbish like repeats of "Will and Grace", "It's Me or the Dog", "Ten Years Younger", "You Are What You Eat" etc. without any form of guilt or fear of rebuke. You also don't have to watch any sport you're not remotely interested in or don't understand. These include Snooker which of course I *understand,* but can anyone explain why you would want to watch this? Is it the players' magnetic personalities, the nail-biting excitement or the roar of the crowd? It's beyond me. I mean, even I can see the attraction of topless darts but the normal variety, oh come on! Football, oh dear Lord, football! As if it's not bad enough, it's the World Cup this year and once more no doubt we'll see our England team "pottering about with the ball" whilst all the other teams - including countries you never knew existed - will enter the field with fighting spirit, ready to take on all comers and actually win. Now, I love tennis but don't get me started on Tiny Tim. A bowl of porridge is more consistent and probably more fun to be around. I absolutely loathe the fact that Timid Tim, who was hilariously dubbed "Tiger", is our tennis ambassador. He's rubbish, he's devoid of personality, he's upper class and worst of all he's called "TIM". You couldn't have found a better stereotype of a "British" tennis player if you tried. I'm with Andy Murray all the way. Okay he's actually Scottish, but if we can claim Rudesdski as English then Andy is positively a local.

Food

At last you no longer have to wait for anyone to get home before you eat. You can also go on the cabbage soup diet without the necessary side effects causing you massive embarrassment. In fact, any diet is just soooo much easier to do when you're single. Or perhaps is it that when you're single you're more paranoid about how thin/fat you are hence you diet more? Actually, thinking about it, I do always gain a few extra pounds when going out with someone or living with them. Ahaha, it's a fact - it's healthier to be single!

Washing

Yes ladies, we all do it. No matter how "equal" we pretend to be in a relationship. I guarantee we ALL (well most of us) do our man's washing. So on a twice-weekly basis that man you love, adore, respect, cherish, admire and so on and so forth, pales ever so slightly when you pick up a pair of skiddy undies! No boyfriend, no pants. Hooorrrayyyy! Actually I miss them ... yeah right.

Sleep

You may well think this could explain why I'm single but I like my sleep and I need at least eight hours in order to function. Therefore, when I go to bed, I go to bed to sleep. At no point do I ever say "I'm tired, I'm off to bed for sex now, coming?" Why is it then that men seem to mishear what I say and presume that when they join me in bed, or if they come to bed with me, that I was lying? That in fact I was not tired at all. In fact they always seem to think I'm bluffing and really meant I wanted to stay up for another hour or so shagging. Bed after 10pm on weekdays is for SLEEPING. On account of the fact that I've worked for eight hours and commuted an hour either side of that and I'm very TIRED. If you wanted sex you should have jumped into bed with me the minute you got home or even better done it on the dinner table, kitchen floor, stairs, ANYWHERE but the bed. Why are men so unimaginative? When single you also don't have to fight for the duvet like your life depended on it, using all manner of tricks in the winter months, e.g. "full body weight manoeuvre" (tuck your end of the duvet underneath your entire body and sleep on it) to the "stick as close to him as you can" trick (if he has all the duvet and you're never separated you will by default have duvet) or, during the summer, constantly be fending off random duvet attacks as he chucks it off himself and doubles the amount you have and don't want. Don't even get me started on snoring. IT'S A DISEASE WITH NO CURE. Men who snore should be made to wear a tattooed disclaimer on their forehead.

Checking In

You are no longer required to let anyone know where you are or who you're with. Nope, the world is in fact your lobster. However, the down side to this does mean if you are murdered, mugged and buried somewhere, no one will have the foggiest notion where to start looking!

Absolutely the last "Sell-By" dates:

81. It takes you 6 months of eating next to nothing to lose 6 pounds yet you can gain 6 pounds in less than 6 hours!

82. Your nieces and nephews are married and have children!

83. The first thing you think of when someone mentions a date is a sweet delicious fruit.

84. Your mum says things like "If you worked as hard at getting a boyfriend as you do everything else, you'd have one by now".

85. Clothes, shoes and bags are now purchased on their comfort and practicality merits in muted colours that will go with everything.

86. You long for the day when you're on the last train home after a night out and there's a man in a car waiting to take you home safely.

87. You wonder why Paul McKenna hasn't produced a book, CD and DVD entitled "I Can Make You Married". [P.S. McKenna no "I Can Make You Have Hair" Book or DVD?]

88. Even in your dreams you are single.

89. You're considering becoming a single mum by adopting - sadly you're not Angelina Jolie so you fear the adoption services may not be so enthusiastic about your single application.

90. You're starting to believe that the conspiracy is this: honest, intelligent, good looking, tall single men are hidden all year round and Harrods sells them in the New Year sale. It now makes perfect sense why the queue is so enormous and women sleep there overnight in order to be first through the door.

91. You wonder how much longer you'd rather be alone than with someone who likes you - but you can't stand.

92. Men your own age are only interested in woman ten years younger. The age bracket of men who would consider a woman your age is 55-75!

93. You know how to bleed radiators, hang pictures and can use the hedge cutters confidently and without maiming yourself, others or small animals.

94. You jump out of your skin if there's an unannounced knock on the door - nobody just turns up anymore.

95. Not only do you burp out loud but you try and say as much of the alphabet as possible whilst burping and your record is G.

96. You've notice a few hairs growing round your nipples and you've decided to let them grow. Your boobs now look like a pair of eyes with billowing, long luscious eyelashes Max Factor would die for.

97. You clean the bath and shower whilst you have a bath or shower. Two birds with one stone!

98. You've acquired some liver spots and are vainly hoping that you'll get enough of them to achieve the look of an overall tan.

99. You've been known to pick your nose and wipe it on the back of your other hand to take to the bin later or when "Homes under the Hammer" has finished.

100. You admit you sometimes forget you've done number 99 and the only way to remove it, once dried, gives the fine hairs on the back of your hand a tiny wax as it peels off.

I realise that I'm riddled to the point of rotting with neurosis. Perhaps I should start again:

Profile:

Hi my name's Jo. I am a hypocritical, self obsessed cow with no redeeming features who would like a perfect man to love her, hold her and tell her not to worry any more because everything is going to be all right despite her many and varied shortcomings!

I'm beginning to realise that I'm not just scared, it's far worse. I'm terrified. I have only had one long-term relationship. That, as you know, was when very young, naïve and innocent. As my innocence and naivety about life slipped away I seemed to morph effortlessly into a hard-nosed, unforgiving, selfish and often angry person. Okay, so I've been hurt, lost people I loved and had my heart broken several times - but who hasn't? I've become paralysed with the fear of being hurt. I look for faults and excuses not to meet people and get to know them romantically simply because I don't feel robust enough to cope with losing them again. It's easier to find the fun in other people's genuine pleas for friendship and love than examine why I feel the need to trivialise it.

Humour

It's been an escape route and defence mechanism for so long, I don't even notice I'm doing it. Everybody likes "Funny Jo". "Life and Soul of the Party" Jo. "Always doing Something Crazy" Jo. What nobody sees is that "Funny Jo" is an alter ego. Would the real Jo Burke please stand up? Of course she won't. She's the last person to stand up and be counted. She's the one that finds every day a struggle and always has. Who has moments of blackness that would scare off the most valiant prince. Nowhere in any language does a fairytale end with; "So Prince

Charming married Princess Unstable Mabel despite her frequent mood swings, her constant need for approval, her swearing and burping".

Me and My Shadow

Wow. That was deep man! Oh go away! *Nope can't make me go away.* Why are you picking on me now? *I hope you don't think you're getting off the "I'm an absolute cow" hook by claiming boo hoo "a broken heart" or "tears of a clown" ha ha nice try.* Shut up. I'm not all bad, as you well know. *It's true she can be quite nice. 1992 was a good year I recall!* Shhh. I'm still writing you know. I haven't finished. *If you haven't, you should before they call doctors for you.* The difficulty is, once you've built a huge, incredibly strong fortress-like wall around you, how do you knock it down? Perhaps I should see a doctor, take Prozac and catapult myself over. Or I could see an analyst of some description and dig a tunnel underneath the walls. Another alternative might be to brick by brick make enough room for the original Jo Burke, the happy go lucky twenty-one year old version, the optimistic, ready for anything Jo Burke to squeeze through. *You'd need to take out more bricks than you think.* Cheers. Even I can't be nice to me so why would any one else? *You'd like to switch me off wouldn't you?* Yes! Yes! YES! You are irritating, rude and interfering. *Yes indeed I am.* Why? *You hate me don't you?* Yes...no...sometimes. *Yes or no?* I am loathed to admit it but I do find you amusing and comforting SOMETIMES. In fact I'd be lost without you. *How sweet. Would you be lost or happier?* Happier? Not happier - you're funnier than me. *Funnier or your worst enemy? Narcissus may have fallen in love with his reflection, but you - you've become obsessed with your subconscious. You've cultivated me to such an extent that you spend more time floating around in your head having imaginary conversations with me than living for the moment in the REAL world.* No I do not... Okay, Okay you got me. I know I do. I also know that the moment I clap eyes on a potential date I work out a millions different reason why it wouldn't work. Too short, too bald, too ginger, too fat, too quiet, too loud, too late, too complicated.

Case in point, the last guy I met years ago under "normal" circumstances in a bar rather than via a computer; He was quite nice looking and asked for my number. We went out again. I noticed he was actually - this will get you - GINGER, yet low and behold still attractive. We have a great time together, laugh loads, really good fun. During the evening though I find out that he comes from a wealthy family and doesn't work (doesn't need to) and has never had a "proper" job in his life. I immediately make the decision that it would never work. He has a posh accent - mine is very Sarf London. His family are minted - I come from a council estate. How can someone that's never had to work understand someone that's currently juggling four jobs just to keep afloat? Yes, I fancied him, yes he seemed to reciprocate, but me in my wisdom couldn't see past all the hurdles I'd put in the way. I steered clear of someone I was attracted to because I couldn't bear the thought of falling madly in love with him then his parents telling him "Dharling she's a fine filly, perfect dalliance but not long-term material" then smile knowingly and say "Oh, did I mention Clementine Carberry-Long is single again?". I don't want to always be the Chorus Girl.

The truth is if I met someone now (not that it seems likely!) I'm not entirely sure what I'd do. The last boyfriend I disastrously lived with scared me into never wanting to move into someone else's home again. So now I finally have my own home, my own space, that no one can tell me to leave (except the bank). So I feel safe. No one can get me. My real concern now is that the last sentence is truer than I would like. I'm just a lonely woman. The only really funny thing in this book is that for every poor lovelorn soul I criticise, every joke I crack or snipe I make, another brick has gone up on my wall. When the roof goes on I'm done for!

* * * * *

Hold the Front page! What's This? Another Chance?

Hurrah and hazzar! You may not believe this but I'm actually going on a bona fide date. As in a "normal" date. You remember - one where a guy you've met asks you out? This is my chance. Perhaps he'll be the one? Well, I was out with some friends when they introduce me to this guy … I think *hmmm, you are quite cute*, smile and then spend the rest of the evening avoiding him. I know, I know but believe me if I didn't find him attractive I would've been more than happy to chat away and behave normally. It's a joke. Anyway he does end up sitting next to me and we do actually chat and he seems okay although we only spoke for a short while as it was the end of the evening. I did however, probably, on reflection, not leave him with best of goodbyes. You see, I was on antibiotics owing to an ongoing dental issue that I won't bore you with. Therefore, when he noticed as we were all leaving that I'd not been drinking, I rather foolishly - and a little too enthusiastically - said "I'm on antibiotics". Now granted had I stopped there, naturally this would be more than acceptable. Sadly I decided to continue and say, whilst clutching at my groin, "It's OK, it's almost all cleared up now". You see? I've not been around men I like for so long I completely forgot that I'm supposed to remain enigmatic and charming, especially when trying to make a good first impression. He of course didn't laugh (I would have done) - he just cocked his head to one side and looked at me rather seriously before leaving. Damn, damn, damn it.

Obviously, owing to me giving it away in the heading and first two sentences, you won't be surprised to learn that a week later I got a call from him asking me out on a date. He'd asked our mutual friend for my number. How cool is that? A man likes me enough to track me down. Yipppeeeee. He was quite formal on the phone and I must admit didn't ask me anything about myself whilst chatting on about his life copiously. But nobody's perfect and I put it down to shy babbling. I can't talk about making an impression after my crotch-clutching, antibiotical, mood killing antics. Basically he's sooo busy that he has to book our date three weeks in advance for which he apologises. Hey, no complaints from me - it's a date a proper date. Fantastic!

* * * * *

Fast forward three weeks:

It's the evening before the date. *Hmm*, I think to myself. *I thought he might have phoned or sent me a text before now to confirm or maybe just to chat.* But just as I'm having doubts the phone rings and it's him! He casually tells me that he was indeed thinking of postponing our date tomorrow as he is so busy - but then he tells me he decided it would after all be nice for him to let his hair down and have something to eat out and a good drink. The reason he's so looking forward to eating out is because he currently has no kitchen and is waiting for the new one to be fitted. Now, call me old fashioned but I'm again feeling quite perturbed by this man. He calls nonchalantly the evening before our, may I remind you, three weeks in advance date and tells me he was going to leave it to the last minute to cancel but on the other hand, as he's got no kitchen and needs to eat, we may as well still meet up! How very dare he? Also there's a distinct lack of any polite enquiry into my life or how I am. So I'm beginning to think I let him off lightly by putting his initial phone rudeness down to nerves. Bizarrely I don't complain and make all the right noises and say I'm looking forward to it. Truthfully, deep down I have serious doubts. Anyway it's done. We agree to meet at 8pm the next day for food and a drink. Oh well, nothing ventured nothing gained.

* * * * *

The Date: 7.45pm

As is well known by now I am as ever running early as I live fairly close to the pub, although not within walking distance. I decide to throw caution to the wind and order a cab and leave the car behind. The cab arrives and I pull up outside the pub dead on 8pm. I am starving, excited and happy. The cab driver said I smelled nice and asked me if I was meeting my boyfriend. I was truthful and said it was a first date. I literally had one leg out the door when my phone rang. It's him. *Ahhh*, I think briefly before I answer. *He's probably been inside for the last ten or fifteen minutes and is checking that I'm coming.* I answer. Would you believe he announces without an apology that he's just indoors "wolfing" some food down but the cab is ordered and he won't be long. Now I'm sure I need not point out that there are several things glaringly wrong with this scenario:

1. He is at home at precisely the time he should be in the pub.

2. He is eating in his home without me.

3. He lives at least twenty minutes away and is not even on his way.

4. He is eating.

5. HE SHOULD BE IN THE PUB.

6. He doesn't seem in the least bit bothered that I am there and starving.

7. HE IS AT HOME EATING!

ARRRRRRRGGGGGGGGGGGGGGGGGGGGGGGGHHHHHHHH HHHHHHHHH. Every bone in my body wants to yell at him. YOU RUDE, SELFISH, HORRIBLE MAN. FORGET ABOUT COMING AND DON'T CALL ME AGAIN. That's what I really want to say. But in my head I can hear all my friends and family saying "So how was the date then?" and me replying "Oh he pissed me off. He was late etc. etc." and then their chorus of response chiming "No wonder you're single - he was only late. You're too hard on them. You don't give anyone a chance". So in order to stop the chorus of disapproval I say, quite grumpily, "Well, I'm going back home as you'll be over half an hour and I'm not hanging around in the pub that long on my own. Give me a call when you're there and I'll drive over".

8.05pm

Back indoors again - even the cab driver couldn't believe it. How embarrassing. Life would be so simple if I fancied the cabby. Anyway I go inside and stuff my face with all manner of naughty things purely because I'm hacked off and somewhere in my psyche I think it will be of enormous benefit to not only be hacked off but obese and suffering with indigestion.

8.10pm

He texts me to say he's in the cab and will drive by and pick me up. Slightly redeemed but still firmly and deeply on the hook with little sign of ever getting off it!

8.45pm

I hear a beep outside. It's him. Perhaps I should have been born in the 1800's or something as I really do appreciate manners and everyone in those days simply dripped good manners. My issue, now that he's already got my back up, is that now it seems to be far too much bother for him to haul himself out of the cab and knock on my door, maybe apologise, and escort me to the cab and perhaps open the cab door. Just as this is going through my head there are now three louder beeps, followed almost immediately by him calling me on my mobile (let us not forget he's in the car directly outside) to say, would you believe, that he's in the car directly outside! Now he's been waiting perhaps at most two minutes and, correct me if I'm wrong, but he's a whole forty-five minutes late and I have in fact already been to the pub once and paid a round trip cab fare. It takes a particularly brave man after doing all that to start getting impatient with me!

8.47 pm

I get in the cab. No "You smell or look nice", just a huge smug smile on his face which completely irritates me. I quite literally have to sit on my hands in order to prevent them from punching the smile off his face on and onto the cab window. There's still no sign of an apology either so as you can imagine it's a difficult journey. He eventually tells me the reason he was running late.

I'm all ears waiting to hear tales of de-railed trains, ambulances, fire engines, last minute presentations or family illness. He calmly tells me he was trying to change a light bulb that had shattered. I kid you not folks. You can't make this stuff up. Sadly, extremely sadly, it really does happen and it would appear only to me. Finally I break and tell him how rude and ill-mannered I thought his behaviour had been. He says he was only late and that the first drink was on him. THE FIRST FECKING DRINK. Ohhhh why didn't he say? If only he'd said all along that all this nonsense meant that I wouldn't have to buy the FIRST FECKING DRINK then it would have been different. Thankfully we pull up outside the pub. He asks the cab driver how much and he rummages in his pockets for a while and then ... wait for it ... this is a gem ... asks me if I have any money to pay for the cab as he doesn't have any cash on him. Score! Way to go Jo. You really do know how to choose them. I gave him a look that should have penetrated his very soul, said "You really put a lot of thought and planning into this evening didn't you?", then I paid the driver. He did immediately go over to a cash point and pay me back.

We then entered the pub and true to his word he did buy the first drink. Now again you may well be thinking; why didn't you go home? Well believe me I would have done at so many points if it wasn't for that damn "chorus". We take a seat and he then continues to talk relentlessly about himself, his family, his work, his up coming holiday, his new kitchen, his new bathroom, the book he's reading. I could go on. I decide he's actually never going to ask me a single question or attempt a conversation. So I interrupt his monologue with; "I'm quite busy too. I have four jobs, I'm an actor, an IT Resourcer, a freelance creative and I run a small Karaoke/DJ business". There I'd said it - surely now he would have to respond. Respond he did with; "Really, oh you should see the place I'm going to in France next week". I officially want to kill him, myself and everyone. I drink all of my large glass of wine practically in one go. How could one - not all, just one - of my jobs not be of interest or worth enquiring about further? HOW? He then does something which really finishes me off. Now, as I said, he's a friend of a very good friend of mine. They happen to be photographers. They do my head shots for me. They are a fab couple and I love them dearly. Now they told me that he was booked in for some photos because he was going to try internet dating and wanted decent ones. So I try the old honestly test. I interrupt his flow again by saying that I've tried internet dating but that I'd not found it successful. He point blank lied. He said he would never try it and that it was like buying bacon in Tescos. So I replied that it was a bit like a meat market ... I'd barely finished the sentence when he interrupted me with. "I never said it was a meat market". I am stunned. No. I point out that he said it was like, and I quote, "buying bacon in Tescos". He continues with it's not the same as saying it's a meat market and I finally snap.

9.35pm

I stop him mid sentence and say the following:

"You are the most ill mannered, rude, selfish, arrogant, boring, self absorbed human I have ever had the displeasure to meet. If you would kindly do at least one gentlemanly thing this evening and escort me to the cab office in order to get me away from you as quickly as possible that would be appreciated".

I also added, after looking around and realising that I was in fact already standing and raising my voice a little with my coat half on and struggling to find the second sleeve:

"Yes I am drunk and do you know why? Because I just downed a large glass of wine on an empty stomach because WE WERE SUPPOSED TO BE GOING TO DINNER!"

9.45pm

Back home. Tipsy. Depressed and dialling my friend Kate to forlornly cry down the phone;

"It was a disaster. Even men that don't even know me treat me like shit!"

That, ladies and gentlemen, was the end of my first proper date in about three years. Am I mad? Should I be putting up with that sort of behaviour? Is everyone else? I mean are there women out there actually so desperate and grateful for male company that they politely laugh and smile at the feckless way their men behave?

APPEAL: I am Jo's dog. Please someone be her
boyfriend so she will stop dressing me up like an idiot.

Epilogue

Of course, I always expected I'd write a book. I'm hoping this book will be a huge success and perhaps boost my acting career. Just like my upside-down backward entrance into the world, I've published a "sort of" autobiography before most people have even heard of me! Well, anyone can do things the right way round. If I've been successful and this has been published - and you've actually purchased this book with your hard earned cash as opposed to finding the draft manuscript on a train - my life must be on the up. Perhaps I might be on my way to dropping down to just three jobs. Or have I just added 'Author' as the fifth? Shit... Anyway my point is if you haven't been too put off by what I've written about myself and you just happen to have a lovely, single, brother, friend or ex that would be perfect for me, do let me know. Much appreciated. Also, I should take this opportunity to thank you for choosing this book and I do hope it didn't disappoint...Actually thinking about it, even if you have found this on a train please still let me know if you know any eligible men that might be of interest. It would be a funny story to tell our grandkids... *Stop it!* What? *You're doing it again leaping too far forward for goodness sake you are NOT going to meet someone by leaving this on a train.* How do you know? *I give up!* Oh and if you did find this manuscript instead of purchasing it, thanks for bothering to read it - let me know what you thought.

I was perhaps egotistically hoping my autobiography would be called hhhmmm... now what would I call it? **"Acting Up" by Jo Burke.** It would be full of inspiring, witty, bittersweet anecdotes from my long and successful career as an Oscar-winning actress or more realistically a TV Soap Awards waitress. Believe me this book is based firmly in reality - if you are single and are thinking about logging on, you would no doubt prefer me to tell you: "Only joking, I am now happily married to a six foot, handsome, successful businessman who adores me and our first child is on the way all thanks to the internet." Gush Gush. However, as you're aware, I'm an honest "girl next door type" apparently, and would loathe to deceive anyone. I would point out that I really do know people who have met and had long term relationships with people they met via the internet. Why, even my own brother - who's been married for twelve years and has three gorgeous children - met his wife through the earlier and now slightly antiquated medium of personal ads. Ironic, really, as he is - and was then - a computer whiz that spent almost every waking hour in front of a screen, which was why he never actually got out to meet anyone in the first place! My mum and the rest of my family would berate him for not going out enough and that he'd never meet anyone unless he did. Now it's reversed and all the single guys and girls are probably, as you read, hunched over a laptop sending messages to random strangers in the hope that they'll find that significant other. I don't consider it embarrassing or anything to be ashamed of. It is truly increasingly difficult to meet new and interesting people in these busy times. I certainly met some during my time on these sites. Well, at least they were new. So my conclusion is that I am in fact too scathing, selfish, sarcastic, honest, fussy, independent, challenging for most men out there with the sad exception of bald, obese, midgets who are queuing up to take me on. Those feisty short, fat slap heads - you gotta love 'em! I suspect I'll have to be patient and wait; either for my eyesight, which is currently 20/20, to fail sufficiently so that these people become attractive or alternatively stop going to the gym, eat everything I want in great quantity, start sporting leggings and baggy T-shirts. Only time will tell.

FAIRYTALE ENDING

I would like to offer apologies now to any Americans or other sensitive types who may be reading this as it does not have the traditional more palatable "happy ending". Don't be too disappointed though because I can guarantee that if they ever make a Hollywood film of the book, I will of course not only be deliriously but hilariously happy. My husband will have teeth inhumanly perfect and so white I can only approach him wearing shades. I'll no doubt be represented by an actress far more beautiful, three stone lighter than me (even if I only weighed three stones!) and a foot taller. Is it too much to ask for Angelina Jolie? *Yeah right Jo like she'd have trouble finding a bloke.* What about Meg Ryan? Oh, humour me, will you? For crying out loud can't a girl talk to herself and dream? I'm off to buy a cat.

THE ONE THAT GOT AWAY

'What happened to Hugh?' I hear you cry. Well, after a good emailing start, we never did meet because his parents announced they were getting divorced. Whilst I agree this can be traumatic for youngsters, I feel it's not something that has quite the same impact on a thirty-something's life. Actually, now I come to think about it, perhaps it was just an elaborate way of cancelling our meeting. You decide.

SELF PUBLICITY AT IT'S BEST!

A few final examples as to why - even with the, so-called, advantage of internet dating - I remain not only single but also bewildered ...

Ad 1:

Hi, I'm an easy going guy wiith a passion for liffe. I have a varried list of intereests, and am equaly hapy staaying in with a film and a nice meel or going out meating new poeple. I enjoy getting away from things, and love finding new places to visit. I am loooking for a funn and affectonate person for new freindship. Oh, and I can't spel. Seriously, I am a honest and decent person and am looking for someone who can return and respect that. I do have two young kids, who are my life and who mean the world to me. I would love to meet someone who I can enjoy life with, someone who I can have a laugh with and someone genuine.

Ad 2:

i need a good woman,and i am a good man, i will be happy to have a her,thanks

Ad 3:

I am fat, lazy, boring and thick and when i'm not gorging myself on butter and watching Trisha I like nothing more than to sit and stroke my collection of pet tarantulas while listening to celine dion.

Ad 4:

HI THE REASON IAM HERE IS MAYBE I WILL FIND THE PERSON IVE ALWAYS DREAMED OF DONT MEAN MISS WORLD BUT FUNNY GOOD LOUGH NICE TO BE WITH CUZ I HAVE ALL DOES THINGS IN ME SO LETS FIND EACHOTHER OK ALL THE BEST FOR US ALL

Ad 5:

I have a burning curiosity about womankind. I find women both beguiling, sometimes quite facinating, occasionally alarming but mostly perplexing. I can analyse and reason, I can parallel park a car and read a map. But these skills seem to have little relevance to understanding relationships. I envy emotional intelligence and despair of stupidity. I hope to learn enough to tip the balance of in the right direction.

Ad 6:

I'm Just a gigolo everywhere I go people know the part I'm playing

Paid for every dance selling each romance Oh what their saying

There will come a day

And youth will pass away What will they say about me

When the end comes I know they'll say just a gigolo

Life goes on without me

Ad 7:

Hola! Yo estoy buscando amistades o mas. Yo vivo en londres pero soy de irlanda. Me gusta a viajar mucho y salir con mis amigos. Si quieres conocerme? escribanme!

hasta pronto

Ad 8:

Hi,

If you have just come back from another date where you have either:

Been bored to tears

Person did not look like his picture

Person didn't stop talking about himself

He didn't stop looking at your chest instead of your face,

He has put on about 3 stones since his photo

He kept talking about his ex partner all night.

A few people have come forward to add to the list with the following, thanks you so much, please keep them coming

He was married

Picture was taken 10 years ago

If there are any others I have missed on the list above please do tell me.

Ad 9:

Please allow me to introduce myself I'm a man of wealth and taste

I've been around for a long, long year Stole many a man's soul and faith. So if you meet me.

Have some courtesy

Have some sympathy, and some taste Use all your well-learned politesse

I consider myself an honest and lively person. I'm not looking for stupid games, but for a nice person.

Ad 10:

hi im fun to be i the like the country side divorce with no children got a good paid job looking to meet a white woman slim and who is fun to be with i like going to a farm in a little farm in east sussex going the local pubs having a meal listerning to groups in one pub

like sitting and enjoying the views and all the wild animals

i also enjoy hunting and shooting down on the farm i guess im a country boy at heart

ive got my own internet business which is doing ok at the mo

if you would like to know more email me what have you got to loose

Ad 11

I'm introvert by nature but I fight it. I place mental compatability above physical looks, but I do insist on blue eyes, unless you're Latin, in which case I accept brown. I can do convincing impressions of various high profile Tory politicians (if there still is such a thing)

Preferably you'd rather spend an evening talking to me than shouting obove the din of some god-awful gentrified south-London club. However, I would never rule out an evening of ecstatic dancing assuming you're drunk enough not to notice me slipping of to the bar.

Ad 12

wicked,sometimes impatient,but loyal looking for someone to go out and play with.i am equally at home in big cities and the countryside.my primary interests are my horses.

Ad 13

I'm a swinger are you a swinger? I am looking for a woman who might, only once we are in a happy committed relationship, have an interest in the swinging lifestyle.

Ad 14

Let's be honest. I drink a lot, I swear a lot and I don't give a shit about what your hopes and dreams are. I'm looking for a smart, sexy, funny lady who can teach me some shit, knows how to laugh and will let me drive. And don't have a dog, because I hate dogs.

Ad 15

Cynical idealist seeks walking contradiction with nice smile, sense of humour and passionate outlook to help him with his agoraphobia. No ugly birds.

I couldn't resist a quick response to lucky number 15:

Hi Cynical

I am a wheelchair bound vertigo sufferer who works as a stunt plane wing walker. I am the love child of Les Dawson and Mo Mowlam. I won't be helping you with your agoraphobia as I think its best for everyone that you stay in.

Jo

AND SO THE END IS NEAR

I will let this chap, the last person to view me, have the final word so you can decide whether or not internet dating is for you!

35-year-old man

seeking women 24-43

About me and what I'm looking for

I have reached a point of clarity in my life where the concept of a relationship is a wonderful and necessary goal, not an oppressive burden. I have spend over ten years building security and maturity, and now I would like a good companion with whom to share these things. I work quite hard at what I do, but I take great pains to develop myself outside of earning a living. I value honesty and communication over pretty much all else. Second comes health and fitness. I work out daily and practice fencing. However, I'm not a muscle-head. I am the eternal student, ever seeking, asking questions, expanding my consciousness and understanding of many fields. My background is in the Humanities (Language, Literature, Art, History, Archaeology, etc.) and some Sciences. I graduated from college years ago, but I never stopped looking for answers. In short, I try to be the classical ideal of a "sound mind in a sound body." My match should also value these things. "Chemistry" is an over-rated myth, a falsehood people desperately want to cling to. I've been fooled by it in the past, and my former blind belief in it has led me down rocky, bitter paths. It's got to be about specific issues of compatibility. But then again, I'm sure most guys would say that. :) Maturity. More important than a woman's calendar-age is her emotional age. This is impossible to see from a mere photo, or first- impression. It takes a great deal of time to learn about who she really is, and I am very willing to give her that time. I prefer women who are single, never married, no children, no smoke (Human ashtrays, begone!), no drama, no racists, no divas. Baggage should be stowed away and not brought into the cabin. She must have solid values, but not be a religious zealot. I have dated women of different backgrounds, and am open-minded. I expect the same enlightened attitude in her as well.

You should know me well enough by now to appreciate how painful it is for me not to comment on his profile. Please insert your own comments here:

_____

_____

_____

_____

I WILL SHUT UP AFTER THIS, I PROMISE

Now of course those listed were not the only dates I went on during that period. Oh no there were many more. Like the alcoholic whose ex wife lived in an annex at the bottom of his garden. The man who claimed to be between 5'9 and 6 foot and was in reality what I can only describe as a tall dwarf and that's being generous. I also did meet many, very sweet, shy and mousey guys who were all too nice, too sweet and definitely too mousey for the likes of me. The sex-obsessed Dutch guy who kindly suggested I should have a boob job. Let's not forget the guy with the throbbing thick blue vein across his nose that actual appeared to have a pulse and was I presume Photoshopped out of his photos. The guy with a sweating problem. The guy with the facial tick. The list goes on ...

In my thirty-four years of existence (although to be fair for at least fifteen of those years I wasn't aware of boys) I've had dates and/or relationships with the following; my school sweetheart, someone from work, normal guys I've met in social situations, speed dating, internet dating and friends or friends ... and nothing, nada, zip, nil points, zero, sweet FA, Zilch. I'm a modern day Miss Haversham whether I like it or not. If I swap my dog for an American Pitbull called Stella that's been trained to seize everything that looks remotely male, then I'm all set!

My tombstone shall read:

Here lies MISS Jo Burke

"No one can say she didn't try"

p.s. "except her friends and family who all thought she could have made more effort and been less fussy" R.I.P

p.p.s "even Miss Haversham managed to get someone to agree to marry her".

Since writing this book Jo has become a successful stand up comedian despite saying it was something she would never do. Never say never ...

Jo's first comedy creation was Mary Magdalene - a depressed, Irish, alcoholic spinster who wears a wedding dress every day "to cheer herself up". So Jo's family finally got to see her in a wedding dress after all.

If you've enjoyed this book please do leave a review on Amazon - it really does help a first timer and if Jo is allowed to write a second one you'll know you've played a massive part and others will know who to blame. Thank you!

Don't forget you can follow Jo on Twitter and Facebook:

JoBurkeComedy

* * * * *

Finalist
Gilded Balloon "So You Think That's Funny?"

"Miranda Hart has strong competition"
Remote Goat

"Burke is clearly very talented, oozing charm and confidence."
Broadway Baby

"Jo Burke showed off her pleasing whimsy, all cuteness hiding a sly edge."
The List

"Jo Burke's Mary Magdalene act stole the show.
Her burlesque piece had me crying."
Simon Donald, Creator of Viz

"Cracking set."
Andy Parsons, Mock the Week

www.joburke.com

APPENDIX

A small useless organ often removed from humans at the whim of a medical professional.

Take that out!

Nope. Anyway I couldn't if I wanted to I am not a Doctor.

ACKNOWLEDGEMENTS

As with everything I've achieved since my dad passed away, this is dedicated to his memory with the knowledge that if he'd read it he would say "You're coming on".

His perpetual "You're coming on" always felt like "You're not good enough" - half insult / half disinterest. Frankly he'd had two boys before me and he knew what to do with them. I came along much later and seemed to completely baffle him as soon as I could speak. My fondest memory is of him carrying a tired but stubbornly trying to stay awake toddler up to bed and singing "Jeepers Creepers, where'd ya get those peepers?" while I fell in and out of slumber. As I got older and more challenging he lost interest in anything I did. I remember he took me to the doctors once and the doctor asked him how old I was - to which he replied eight. I looked up at my dad aghast. I was in fact six. So I said so, to which my dad responded, "Oh that must be the other one I was thinking of". I'm the only girl AND my brothers are eight and ten years older, not two! But of course Dad was never wrong and I just wanted to be good enough.

I'd like to thank my wonderful Mum and brothers for putting up with my madness over the years and helping me out endlessly with life problems, computer problems and house moving problems respectively and for supporting me in everything I do. This includes coming to my early fringe shows and doubling the audience!

Last but not least a big thank you to all my friends who have all in one way or another helped and supported me massively. Special thanks to Ginette Warwick who read the first draft and gave me, as always, her honest opinion and support. You've always been there for me in times of great joy but, more importantly, in times of great sadness. For that I shall always love you like the sister my dad thought I had! X

My thanks also to Shannon Fairchild, Gemma Woolford, Jo Pockett and Manolis Emmanouel who all read early versions.

Now to blame, sorry I mean of course thank, the people without whom this book would never have been published: Jerram Shurville and the ever patient Roy Robart and Amanda Egan. So do please address all complaints to them.